PELICAN BOOKS

FAMOUS
AMERICAN MEN OF SCIENCE

THOMAS ALVA EDISON
JOSIAH WILLARD GIBBS

BY

J. G. CROWTHER

Volume II

PUBLISHED BY

PENGUIN BOOKS

HARMONDSWORTH MIDDLESEX ENGLAND
245 FIFTH AVENUE NEW YORK U.S.A.

First Edition 1937
Published in Pelican Books 1944

MADE AND PRINTED IN GREAT BRITAIN FOR PENGUIN BOOKS LIMITED
BY R. & R. CLARK, LIMITED, EDINBURGH

CONTENTS

ILLUSTRATIONS

v

ILLUSTRATIONS

THOMAS ALVA EDISON
1847–1931

"Then I realized that the telegraph was a great invention"

EDISON
At the Age of Fourteen or Fifteen

I

THE RELATION OF INVENTION TO SCIENCE

THIS book is about certain American men of science. The first question which arises in connection with Edison is his status. He was undoubtedly an inventor. Is an inventor a man of science? Before this question may be answered, it is necessary to discuss whether "man of science" and "scientist" have the same meaning. The first term is broader than the second. "A man of science" means a man engaged in science, or making use of science, whereas the second is usually reserved to describe a person such as a research chemist, who discovers new facts and theories.

Edison was certainly a "man of science" because he worked with the facts of science, though he discovered very few new facts of the conventional scientific type. Nevertheless, he could claim to be a "scientist," even in the strictest sense, as he discovered the Edison Effect, a phenomenon of first-class importance.

It is permissible to contend that a man who creates new instruments, such as the carbon telephone transmitter, with the assistance of the theory of electricity, may be named a "scientist." A new instrument is a new fact in the world of natural existence. In this sense, its status is as good as any other newly-discovered fact of natural existence, such as a new chemical compound.

Sharp distinctions between "scientist," "man of science," and "inventor" are harmful, and to a high degree artificial. Distinctions do exist, but they have been exaggerated, especially by scientists. The features that scientists have in common with inventors are far more important than their differences.

Scientists have tended to exaggerate their difference from inventors for reasons of social prestige. An inventor is engaged in making devices of use to man. He often makes things with his hands. He is closely connected with manual workers and business men. He tries to make devices which are profitable.

The scientist frequently claims that his researches are inspired by pure curiosity, and may have no practical value.

He considers that he exercises his intellect solely to increase the dignity of the human mind, and not to serve any other human interests. He exaggerates these features in order to magnify the distinction between his aims and those of manual workers and business men. He wishes to become identified with the aristocratic leisure class, who receive salaries without duties, and are under no compulsion to do useful work. He desires to inherit the prestige of the magician, who could command nature without working.

All of these attributes are the traditional qualities of members of the governing class. Scientists claim them because they wish to be included in that class, and not in the working class. As inventors are evidently closely connected with the working class, scientists do not wish to be confused with them.

The orthodox conception of the scientist as distinguished from the inventor is permeated with the traditional ideas of the superiority of mind over matter, of theory over experiment, and other principles inherited from prehistoric magic, which have been rationalized, for instance, in Plato's philosophy.

The acceptance of this conception makes the history of science unintelligible. It is impossible to understand why particular scientific theories were studied at any particular time without considering their relations to contemporary inventions and technology. Theory and practice cannot be studied apart. The full importance of the discoveries of Faraday and Clerk Maxwell was not clear until inventors, such as Edison and Marconi, had proved that they were of profound value, and were far more than ingenious intellectual tricks. The separation of science and invention has obscured the origin and nature of science, and through this has retarded the growth of an adequate philosophy of history. If the rôle of science in history is not understood, then men will not know how properly to use science for the advance of civilization.

There is much evidence in the present condition of the world that man has not yet gained more than a rudimentary notion of the rôle of science in civilization. The failure to understand the ultimate inseparability of science and invention is an aspect of the wider failure to conceive an intelligible history of science.

Henry Ford's conception of the nature of scientists and inventors is more correct than the old view, evolved by scholars of the governing class in aristocratic, pre-mechanical civilizations. He writes (with Samuel Crowther) :

In another age and time, each of Edison's inventions would have been considered either as unique scientific discoveries or as scientific toys. The older scientists made their discoveries as things of themselves and were so far away from the daily workaday world that they would have lost standing had they even suggested the possibility that their studies could have any commercial application. Then Edison came along—a greater scientist than any of them, but without being bound by the old scientific traditions. He was a scientist, but also he was a man of extraordinary common sense. It was a new combination.

Edison thought of science as an aid to mankind and, instead of being a specialist in any one branch, he reviewed every branch in order to assemble and select the best ways and means of accomplishing whatever he had in mind to do. He was not an inventor in the sense that he just thought up certain methods and devices. . . . He was a whole experimental laboratory in himself, and definitely ended the distinction between the theoretical man of science and the practical man of science, so that today we think of scientific discoveries in connection with their possible present or future application to the needs of man. He took the old rule-of-thumb methods out of industry and substituted exact scientific knowledge, while, on the other hand, he directed scientific research into useful channels.

The scientists of the old school have never considered Edison as one of themselves, because he did practical things instead of just making and recording experiments. The engineers have not considered him an engineer, because he never worked on traditional engineering lines. In fact, he is both a scientist and an engineer, and he established the modern spirit in both science and engineering, which is to say that the engineers depend on the scientists and the scientists depend on the engineers.

Ford ascribes too much to Edison, because he credits him with introducing the modern conception of the industrial scientist. Many men before Edison contributed to the evolution of this conception, for it was brought into existence by the steam-age, and was implicit in the writings of Francis Bacon, and the aims of the founders of the Royal Society of London. But by the middle of the nineteenth century the social and utilitarian aims of the founders of post-Renaissance science had almost been forgotten. A new intellectual aristocracy had grown, and apparent uselessness tended to be regarded as a necessary qualification for admittance. The great scientists of the nineteenth century had immense social value, but they were often unconscious of its true nature, supposing that it lay in absence of evident connection with human interests. They considered that science was a disinterested search for pure knowledge, made in order to reveal the ways of Providence, and increase the intellectual dignity of man, or certain men.

Edison came into the current of nineteenth-century technology without having acquired the traditional view of science. He was able to express directly in his own career what society was expecting of science. He was in front of his contemporaries because he had escaped a tradition that was not in consonance with the most progressive social developments.

If Edison had lived at the time when the Royal Society of London was founded, he would have been elected a member before he was thirty years of age. In recent times, inventors such as J. W. Swan, D. E. Hughes, and Charles Parsons were elected to the Royal Society. Edison was not elected a member of the National Academy of Sciences until he was eighty-one years old.

Scientists and inventors have more in common than in difference, so they need not be sharply separated. Their histories should be studied together. Edison discovered only one important scientific fact of the sort discovered by Faraday in scores. He found that electricity is emitted by hot filaments. The operation of the radio valve depends on this phenomenon. This difference between the work of Edison and Faraday would seem to show that they are of entirely different types. But the importance of Faraday's discoveries cannot be explained without reference to the work of Edison and other inventors and engineers, so, in the last analysis, Faraday as a scientist and Edison as an inventor cannot be assessed separately. Both of them were great men of science, of different sorts. This is the explanation why Edison is truly a " man of science."

II

THE ORIGIN OF AMERICAN INVENTIVENESS

EDISON is accepted as the most typical example of an inventor. Why should he have appeared in the United States rather than in any other country ? The first part of the answer is that the United States has been the premier country of invention during the last hundred years. Edison was born in an environment fertile for invention. This circumstance enabled him to surpass equally talented inventors in less encouraging environments. As the majority of the Americans are relatively recent descendants of immigrants from Europe, their genetic constitution is very similar to that of Europeans. There is no evidence that they have some inborn inventive faculty of a sort not possessed by Europeans. The origin of American inventiveness is chiefly found in the circumstances of American history.

The first colonizers of America were the Spanish, and the second were the English. American inventiveness grew out of the second colonization, and is therefore connected with features which distinguish the second from the first. It might be attributed to lack of inborn inventiveness in Spaniards. But Spaniards have made remarkable inventions. At the present time de la Cierva has invented the auto-gyro, and Longoria a method of welding fine wires by exactly measured and controlled currents discharged from condensers. The significant feature of the careers of these Spanish inventors is that they have not developed their ideas in Spain, but in the industrialized countries of Europe and America.

There were fundamental differences between the social structures of the Spanish and the English colonies. The former consisted of settled natives governed by a small class of rich conquerors, who did not introduce any new productive habits. Their aim was to govern, and take wealth from others by force, not to produce wealth themselves. Under these social conditions the governors had no incentive to invent, because they could live well without producing anything themselves, and the natives had no incentive because they had no rights.

The English colonizers came to America a century later, and from a country whose social and industrial system was developing rapidly. Their social philosophy was two or three centuries nearer than the Spanish to modern industrialism. Besides coming from an industrially more advanced country, the English came from different social strata. The New Englanders, whose philosophy ultimately had most influence on the evolution of American ideals, were mainly independent farmers, peasants, and skilled craftsmen, who came to America to acquire the freedom to live as they wished, without interference ; to support themselves by their own work, and to secure to themselves all the profits thereof. They did not intend to exploit conquered natives. Self-help was fundamental in their philosophy. The New Englanders did not believe that manual labour was disreputable. This allowed them to think about the problems of doing things, and see how manual labour, with which they had intimate acquaintance, might be minimized. Slave-owners have little personal acquaintance with manual labour, and are under strong social influence to ignore the details of how it is done. Self-supporting manual workers can increase their profits only by working harder and more ingeniously, whereas slave-owners can increase profits by increasing oppression. Thus the New England colonists and their successors under the influence of the Yankee spirit had a personal interest in labour-saving and profit-increasing devices. They belonged to social classes who had lost the cowed spirit and fatalism of the European labourer. They brought the independence of the European middle classes to bear on the problems of labouring technique. The rise of American inventiveness has been deeply influenced by class psychology and interests. Owing to the richness and emptiness of America these personal interests were stronger than those of their corresponding classes in Europe. The social order of European countries was fixed. England, France, and Holland had populations of fairly stable size, as large as they could support. The incentive to middle- and lower-class production was limited by the privileges of the aristocracy, who could secure through their political power a part of all the new wealth created by other classes.

The social structure of North American society remained fluid for the first two centuries of its existence, owing to the steady extension of the frontier westwards. During this period the population never reached a stable number, as in the European countries. It increased rapidly, and moved continuously in tens of thousands across the continent. Under these continually changing conditions, the American craftsman and independent worker never acquired a fixed conception of his place in the social order. Vast supplies of land and resources were continually available to him for exploitation. His enterprise was not checked by the knowledge that he would inevitably have to share his profits with landowners, and that success in collecting profits would not automatically qualify him for admittance to the governing class.

In these circumstances, it was worth while thinking out ways of increasing productivity and profits.

The social philosophy of the New England colonists was not that of slave-owning classes. In addition, there were no settled natives in the northern states. The land was very sparsely populated. As the intensive systems of farming and manufacture introduced by the Northern Europeans required a relatively dense population for successful operation, there was a large demand for labour, to extend the system in the unpopulated west. The shortage of labour stimulated the invention of labour-saving appliances.

There is a further factor. It is possible that there is some connection between inventiveness and independence of behaviour. The colonizers of America were naturally selected from the more independent members of the European populations, and may therefore have had slightly more than the average amount of inborn inventive ability found among Europeans.

All of these influences interacted from an early date to stimulate inventiveness in North Americans. As E. L. Bogart writes, "what had been an expedient now became a national habit." By the beginning of the nineteenth century, the habit of invention had become thoroughly established, and spread through a large and rapidly increasing population. The stimulating influences still existed and could work upon more human material. By the end of the first half of the nineteenth century, the stream of invention had been raised to a spate. For instance, American inventors revolutionized agricultural implements which had remained essentially unchanged since the days of the Roman Empire. The first important contribution towards the mechanization and modernization of domestic life was made in 1846 by the American invention of the sewing machine. In 1865 American apple-peelers, knife-cleaners, egg-beaters, and clothes-wringers astonished English observers. Morse introduced the recording electric telegraph in 1844.

American inventors were very prominent in the development of the steamboat. They developed the use of interchangeable parts early, and their exhibits at the London Exhibition of 1851 made a deep impression.

The American patent law had democratic characteristics. It allowed the protection of small improvements besides major inventions, so that small inventors, who would have been overawed by the patent law of other countries, were encouraged in America. On the other hand, the administration of American patent law had serious defects. Edison complained that it was far slower and far less competent than English patent law administration. In England cases had to be argued in front of the judges, and the essential points could be brought out quickly. The American judges could decide on written statements, in which the points were frequently lost. Edison said that it was easier to find first-class lawyers with a thorough grasp of scientific ideas in England than in America. The patent law of both countries was easily exploited to the advantage of rich clients. But the American protection of small improvements remained an incentive to the small inventor. It also helps to account for the enormous number of American patents. Edison himself was granted more than one thousand.

The rate of invention in America was much increased during the depression of 1837, and greatly increased during the Civil War after 1860 by the demands for economy and labour-saving.

Edison became mature when the American tradition of invention was a hundred years old, and had reached a period of very rapid growth and intense stimulation. He was the outstanding product of a flourishing tradition created by powerful historical forces, and his apparition in America at this particular date is not surprising.

III

EDISON'S PERSONALITY

THE age of thirty-nine divided Edison's life into two main periods. During the first, as Dyer and Martin observe, his work had the inconsequential freedom and crudeness of pioneer life. Ideas piled on him, and he rushed from one roughly finished invention to the next. In the second he was less brilliant. He married a second time, conducted his social life with more orthodoxy, and became an example of a successful man of the day, a model of the well-to-do American's ideal of a good citizen. His social philosophy was conventional and was adopted from his environment without question. But within the boundaries of these philosophical principles, his personal behaviour was original. The respectability of the latter half of his life did not change his personal originality, and he did not try to imitate the imaginary figure of a cultured, dignified, and benevolent gentleman, created by media of publicity.

Edison was of medium height. His head was abnormally large. His eyes were grey or grey-blue, and in infancy his hair was fair. He had a good colour and quick step. During the thirties he began to arrange his hair in a sweeping lock over the forehead, like Napoleon. His mouth had a rather surly twist, but this was less important in his expression than the power of his eyes. They were very bright when he was interested. Many men felt the domination of his personality from the first moments of contact with him. He employed and retained for decades able men who disagreed with him. He was known as *the Old Man* before he was thirty.

He led a rough but not poor or miserable life up to the age of twenty-three. He had little formal education, so he spoke the language of the masses. He never modified his accent. As he was auto-didactic, and could learn from his experience only, or from someone sharing his interests strongly, he would probably never have acquired a cultivated accent under any conditions. But he became deaf when a boy, which lessened any possibility that he would ever stop using the idiom of his youth. It is said that he could hear noises in which he was specially interested, such as background noises in phonograph records.

17

M. A. Rosanoff joined his staff in 1903, when Edison was fifty-six. He asked him what laboratory rules he should observe. Edison " spat in the middle of the floor and yelled out, ' Hell ! there ain't no rules around here ! We are tryin' to accomplish somep'n ! '" Edison introduced himself to Rosanoff as " Don Quixote," and his assistant J. F. Ott, who had been with him thirty years, as " Santcho Pantcho." His colleagues were described as " muckers," and himself the " chief mucker."

He was an astute judge of character. His hold over others was partly due to his ability to expose their weak points. He utilized this insight to preserve the morale of his staff. Everyone was made to pretend that he was about to solve his problem, even if he was quite at sea. Everyone knew that Edison knew that he was in difficulties and was outwardly more cheerful than the situation justified. The inability to acknowledge this to Edison's face produced a state of guilt and fear that made them work harder than ever. Edison was a master of this auto-suggestive principle of tribal leadership.

He was not sensitive in the immediate handling of truth. He was slow to contradict erroneous exaggerations of his achievements. He said that " we always tell the truth. It may be deferred truth, but it is the truth ! "

His early connection with journalists made him easy-going with the press. This helped the spreading of misleading accounts of his work, which angered many persons, especially academic scientists.

He was of Dutch descent, extremely pertinacious, and had enormous capacity for attention to details. His temperament was sanguine, with some tendency to choler. He began work each day with the openmindedness of a child, and swiftly forgot failures. He could roar with laughter like an aborigine, and sometimes, when seriously vexed, his anger was terrifying. The skin in the centre of his forehead used to be spasmodically rotated in these paroxysms. When thoughtful, he used to pull his right eyebrow.

He had no taste in art, music, or literature, except in telling stories. The parts of his mind concerned with those subjects were arid. He strummed on an organ with one finger. He could not believe the report of one of his phonograph salesmen from Germany, that the Germans demanded records of classical music. He chose banal matter for the stories of the first commercial motion pictures.

The first words spoken by his immortal invention, the phonograph, were : " Mary had a little lamb."

Though without taste, he was lively and jolly. He liked and demanded cheerfulness and optimism. He organized sing-songs among his staff, during long periods of work.

He was fond of stories, and showed skill in telling them. Many were based on personal experiences. The perfection of some of them seems to show that his inventive power was not restricted to mechanics.

Edison accepted the ethics of capitalist commerce. The trade secret of the composition of the wax for his phonograph records was stolen by a trade rival's spy. When Rosanoff, who had proved this by analysis, abused the methods of their rival, Edison was amused.

" What are you so excited about ? Everybody steals in commerce and industry, I've stolen a lot myself. But I knew *how* to steal. They don't know *how* to steal—that's all that's the matter with them."

He adapted himself without difficulty to the bosses of Tammany Hall, when he required municipal permissions for constructing his electric light system in New York.

In his later years he was complacent about the financial methods of Jay Gould. This was probably a partial pose, as he had violently abused Gould when swindled by him in his early years. The pose was made in order to support the class myth of the well-to-do American, that wealth is sacred, however obtained. Edison supported the myth in order to please the rich capitalist friends of his later years. He probably convinced himself that he believed in it. He did not support it in his personal behaviour. He made no money at all out of his greatest inventions, the development of the electric light and power systems. He wished to be a great man, and leave an impression on history. He spent all the money that came to him on the achievement of new inventions to add to his monumental list.

His long hours of work were famous. He worked twenty hours a day for periods of months. When excited by some idea he could work continuously for days. On one occasion he worked continuously for five days and five nights.

He was able to sleep instantly at will, and to wake up instantly half an hour later, refreshed. He never dreamt. He drove his colleagues into working very long hours, which few of them could stand.

On one occasion, when his son felt sleepy, he recommended

him to take a nap under the laboratory bench, from which position he was retrieved by his mother. Edison's resistance to sleep was abnormal, and he could work well with little sleep for long periods. But when he was not pressed, he would sleep nine hours.

In early life, he did not bother about choice of food. In middle age he dieted to keep his weight constant. He ate little meat, and was sparing with food. He smoked large numbers of strong cigars, chewed tobacco, drank much strong coffee, and took no exercise. He lived until he was eighty-four, which was rather shorter than many of his ancestors, so he probably suffered slightly from the effects of his mode of life. His intense intellectual work was not entirely harmless. Like many men who have worked with their hands he was fond of pastry. Manual work requires much energy, which is most easily obtained by eating large quantities of carbohydrates. The habit of pastry-eating often persists in men who have left manual work and entered sedentary professions. In members of the upper classes it is sometimes a mark of the self-made man.

Edison's extraordinary application may have been due to his physiological constitution, but it is possible that he also had psychological motives. His colleagues noted that he seemed to fear to be indolent, as if he had a New England conscience. He records that he had a deep feeling of guilt when a child because he failed to report the drowning of a playmate. Perhaps his efforts were partly an attempt at absolution. He sometimes showed masochistic tendencies, as when he copied out by hand a typewritten report of thirty pages needing only a few incidental corrections, which could perfectly well have been inserted in the typescript and re-typed by his secretary. He had a prodigious memory and an immense knowledge of miscellaneous scientific facts. His method of inventing was empirical, and consisted of trying combinations of these facts, whether or not they had any obvious connection. He said that all experiments were successful, because the knowledge of how a thing was not done was valuable as an aid to the discovery of how it might be done. His knowledge of scientific theory was slight. According to Rosanoff, he did not understand Avogadro's hypothesis. It follows from this that he could not have had a logical understanding of the elements of the atomic theory of chemistry.

He probably had an inferiority complex through his

ignorance of academic science. He was particularly fond of telling stories against academically trained scientists, and jibing at those he employed. He was apt, when he did this, to exaggerate the simplicity of his manners. He defined genius as " One per cent inspiration and ninety-nine per cent perspiration."

His knowledge of science was superficial but very wide, and he was extremely inventive with what he knew. Persistent trying of combinations was probably the best way of exploiting his shallow oceans of scientific facts.

During the first part of his life he dressed carelessly. He appeared as dirty, as any of his labourers. He was unkempt, and often not better dressed than a tramp. His assistants sometimes secretly daubed themselves with grime, in order to give an impression of intense activity, and recommend themselves to his prejudice.

Henry Ford admired Edison's power of driving other men. He echoed his philosophy of hard work and hustle. But his emulation of Edison has not been entirely happy. The strain of working in Ford's factories has broken some men, and prepared them for crime and gangsterism. Edison was not a solemn tyrant. His humour prevented overstrained colleagues from seeking revenge by attacks on society. He was not a doctrinaire, and not insensitive to the feelings of others. He created a new sort of sublimated gangsterism. He was the boss of a gang engaged in blackmailing nature. He oppressed the facts of science until he squeezed inventions out of them. He formed his gang out of men with compensating qualities. He imagined and thought out the experimental attacks. He was not particularly skilful with tools. He was primarily an imaginative thinker. He worked with sketches, and preferred giving instructions by sketch rather than verbally. Some of his assistants were brilliant mechanics and instrument-makers, some were brilliant fitters with exceptional steadiness of hand and patience, who could make provisionary models work. Some were mathematicians and theorists of the highest academic qualifications. These were employed to check the theoretical possibilities of his ideas. His assistants were often required to try things without being told why. This was a typical gangster-like procedure.

Edison could secure the intensest blind loyalty. His gang had confidence in his gifts and leadership. He muscled into invention, in Rosanoff's phrase, like a " happy hooligan."

IV

HIS LIFE AND WORK

1

THE Constitutional Convention of 1787 was dominated by the representatives of the two small but relatively rich classes of planters and traders. After a severe struggle the traders, under the leadership of Hamilton and Madison, persuaded the planters to accept a constitution based on principles favourable to the trading interests. The planters' ablest leader, Jefferson, was absent as American minister in Paris when the Convention began. It had reached a crisis in its proceedings by the date of his return. The opponents of the proposed constitution were still in a majority and Hamilton became desperate at his prospective failure to impose the principles of the traders onto the planters. Jefferson has described how, after his return, and before he had grasped the situation, Hamilton pleaded with him to persuade some of his planter colleagues to change from opposition to support of the adoption of the new constitution. Hamilton suggested that if the planters would accept the constitution, the traders would agree to the establishment of the Federal Government in Virginia, where, owing to geography, it would be under the planters' influence.

Jefferson agreed to this compromise, but soon perceived that he had been outwitted. He and his successors tried to retrieve their ascendancy. They swiftly gained political power, and steadily increased their strength during the next half-century.

Through their control of the Government they were able to minimize the operation of those features of the constitution favourable to traders, but they never felt strong enough to seize economic power and rewrite the constitution according to their own economic interests and principles. They failed to consolidate their power because of the economic strength of their opponents and, among other reasons, the weakness of their own philosophy.

Jefferson is celebrated for the philosophical cast of his mind, yet the tragical mistake of his life was philosophical.

He was outwitted by Hamilton because he had no clear theory of political economy and was unable at once to perceive the theoretical implications in Hamilton's proposals. The defects in his social philosophy arose from his attempts to base the idea of human liberty on the concept of private property ; two ideas that cannot be combined together clearly and satisfactorily.

Jefferson had advanced views on nearly all social questions of secondary importance ; for instance, it is said that he inspired the American patent law, which encouraged Edison and other inventors, but on the question of primary importance, the status of property, he was reactionary. This explains why he and his successors exhibited a combination of attractiveness and futility.

Madison and Hamilton plainly stated that they held private property sacred. Jefferson disliked this worship of private wealth, but he could not suggest any alternative basis for the social structure. He believed that private property in land was healthier than private property in banks and factories.

The struggle between the agricultural and trading classes continued through the first half of the nineteenth century. In that period both classes had grown in economic power and numbers, and the evolution had greatly altered the features of their struggle, though not its essence. By 1860 the traders felt strong enough to abolish the compromise of 1787. They were no longer willing to surrender the social prestige of political power for the substance of a constitution favourable to trade. They wanted both. The agriculturists, who had never had the courage to fight for a new constitution which suited them, now decided to fight for the retention of political privilege. The primarily agricultural states of the South seceded, with the intention of forming their own government and constitution. The primarily industrial states of the North wished to preserve and extend centralized banking, tariffs, and unified distribution favourable to industrial development.

Both sides appealed to high principles of secondary importance when the conflict appeared inevitable. The South accused the North of cultural backwardness, which was partly true, owing to the exclusion of Northern representatives from political leadership. For several decades the South monopolized the chief political appointments. The North accused the South of moral turpitude for practising slavery.

The result of the Civil War was as historically certain as that of the War of Independence. Franklin was confident of ultimate victory because the growth of population and economic power was in favour of the United States. The Northerners could have been equally confident because similar material forces were growing in their favour. Superiority in numbers and equipment finally gave them complete victory.

The circumstances of the War of Independence and the Civil War involved much consideration of the problem of human liberty. Many of the insurgents of 1776 were subsequently disillusioned when they saw that the government of America had passed from a set of rich Englishmen to a set of rich Americans. Like many other revolutionaries they believed they were fighting for liberty and discovered they had achieved only a transference of power. But much of the illusion that the War of Independence was primarily concerned with human liberty has remained, and has haunted America since. Thinkers, such as Jefferson, believed that human liberty might be based on the institution of private property, and assented for that reason to its sanctification in the constitution.

The implications of the combination of the sanctity of human liberty with the sanctity of private property in the constitution were drawn out by the triumphant traders after the Civil War. The military success of the North had demonstrated the superiority of its form of property. Property in land and slaves had to give precedence to property in money and industrial capital, in order that the god of property enshrined in the constitution should, as it were, receive the due sacrifice. At the same time, the other god of human liberty was duly appeased by the liberation of the slaves.

After the Civil War, a governing class of industrial capitalists with little tradition, and believing in the incompatible principles of the sanctity of human liberty and the sanctity of private industrial capital, became free to exploit a rich continent for profit.

2

Thomas Alva Edison was born in 1847, when the social forces which motivated this historical development began to accelerate rapidly towards explosion. The beginning of his adolescence coincided with the outbreak of the Civil War, and he spent his most impressionable years in the midst of one of the greatest social battles in history. His ideas and intellectual conceptions of life, his ideology, were acquired during his adolescence, and are a product of the interaction between his nborn qualities an d his historical environment.

Edison's ancestors were Dutch. They were members of a family of millers which had a considerable business by the Zuyder Zee. They emigrated to America in 1730, and settled on a bank of the Passaic River in New Jersey. By 1776, the date of the beginning of the War of Independence, the settlers had enjoyed some prosperity and grown into an energetic family of colonists. Different members of the family took opposite sides in the war. One Thomas Edison became an American patriot of some importance. He had been an official in a bank on Manhattan Island, and was appointed as a clerk in the office of the Secretary of the Continental Congress. He received authority to sign United States bills of credit, and his signature is found on Continental currency notes issued in 1778. In spite of his eminence he was not clever in personal business affairs, and his debts increased as his status rose.

The traitor Benedict Arnold tried to exploit his situation, and bribe him to commit treason. Edison exposed this action to the Congress, which passed a resolution declaring that " Thomas Edison has by an essential service to the United States and singular proof of his fidelity to their interests, recommended himself to the attention and reward of Congress."

The members voted a sum of money for him. He spent much effort during his remaining years' trying to collect this money, but without success. In 1783 a creditor had him jailed, but he, unfortunately, was unable to jail Congress for debt. He remarked that Congress was " void of all sense of honour or humanity," and if he had rendered assistance to savage tribes he would have experienced far better treatment.

He became dependent on private charity, but lived to the great age of one hundred and four years.

While Thomas Edison was giving important and loyal service to the American insurgents, his relative John Edison was fighting on the side of the British Crown. The biographers of Edison have supposed that John Edison was the son of Thomas Edison. Research by W. A. Simonds seems to show, however, that they were probably brothers or cousins.

When the war started, John Edison was a patroon, or

possessor of estates held under Dutch forms of law, in Essex County. He had married one of the Ogden family and had several children. He was unable to prevent the people in his district from following the insurgents, and fled with his family to New York, which was in British hands. He enlisted in Lord Howe's troops and guided their pursuit of Washington through Jersey. He was presently captured by the Americans. He fortunately had to wait about a year in prison before being tried for high treason. If he had been tried immediately, when feeling was most intense, he would probably have been executed at once. Even after the delay, he was convicted and sentenced to death.

When his wife heard of the sentence, she increased her efforts to secure some mitigation. She was helped by several of her relatives who supported the Americans, and especially by Thomas Edison, the Congressional Clerk. Through their help, John Edison was released on parole. He returned to his family in New York.

When the War of Independence was ended, the colonists who refused to acknowledge the sovereignty of the United States were transported by the British to Nova Scotia. John Edison with his wife and seven children were among the thirty-five thousand persons who preferred to pioneer in the primeval forest rather than submit to the United States. In a former landlord this showed exceptional determination.

Besides migrating into the Nova Scotian wilderness, John Edison tried to obtain compensation for the loss of his American property by petitioning the British Government. Like his relative on the American side, he also failed to receive his due. His claim is extant in the Public Record Office in London. He asked for £388 in lieu of his seventy-five acres, house, black mare, fifteen sheep, and three beehives.

John Edison remained in Nova Scotia for about twenty years. W. A. Simonds has shown that during this period John Edison's eldest son Samuel, who had accompanied him into exile at the age of sixteen, married Nancy Stimpson, and became the father of eight children. One of these was born in 1804, and was named Samuel Edison junior.

About 1811 the Edison family decided to migrate again, to some province more promising and fertile than Nova Scotia. As a British Loyalist John Edison was entitled to six hundred acres of virgin land in Canada. He took his family to New York to visit the Ogdens, and then travelled to the North past Niagara by ox wagon to a place near the present Port Burwell on Lake Huron. The family founded a village in the district and named it Vienna.

In 1812 the United States decided to go to war with the British again, in order to resist the British interference with American trade during the Napoleonic wars.

Regiments of militia were immediately recruited among the Canadians to resist American invasion. John Edison's eldest son Samuel raised a company of volunteers, of which he became captain. Samuel and his comrades successfully resisted the American expeditions, and in a few months returned to the Vienna settlement.

Under the influence and labour of John Edison and his sons Vienna was provided with land for streets, schools, and a cemetery. The Edison house was always left with a meal laid on the table, so that strangers could find food if they called when the family was away.

John Edison probably died about 1814. His bold contests with the opposition of man and nature were aided by a fine physique. He and his sons were all more than six feet tall. They had similar features, and tended to suffer in childhood from a throat affliction.

Samuel Edison became the head of the family. His son Samuel junior, born in 1804, grew up into another strapping man. He was the local athletic champion, especially in running and jumping. He started an inn when he came of age. In 1828 he married an American girl, Nancy Elliot, who was the first schoolmistress to be appointed in Vienna.

She was seventeen years old, and was descended from a family which contained several preachers and a Quaker. She was a sensible woman, as she became popular in spite of being better educated than her neighbours. Nineteen years after her marriage she gave birth to Thomas Alva Edison.

Soon after her marriage, her father-in-law Samuel senior married again, near the age of sixty, and became the father of four more sons and a daughter. He died in Vienna in 1865, at the reputed age of one hundred and three, but was probably only ninety-six. Thomas Alva Edison when five years old was taken to see his old and formidable grandfather. He " viewed him from a distance, and could never get very close to him." He had " some large pipes, and especially a molasses jug, a trunk, and several other things that came from Holland." " He chewed tobacco incessantly, nodding to friends as they passed by." He walked with a very large cane, and resented assistance.

Long before Alva was born, his father Samuel junior was again exhibiting the political intransigeance of the Edisons. Great-grandfather John Edison had fought against the United States, and preferred the loss of a small estate and exile to submission. Samuel junior, the future father of Alva, now raised arms against the Canadian Government. In 1837 an insurgent named W. L. Mackenzie tried to organize a revolt in Canada on the ground of the old American principle of no taxation without representation. Samuel Edison sympathized with Mackenzie, and lent his inn at Vienna for conspiratorial meetings, and became captain of a band of rebels.

Mackenzie and his followers attempted to seize power in Toronto. While Samuel Edison and his men were marching to his support, they heard that Mackenzie had failed and had fled.

It was evident that Samuel Edison would have to suffer exile to Bermuda or escape, so he chose to escape. He quickly returned to Vienna, said good-bye to his family, and ran through the woods for the United States. He covered about one hundred and eighty miles on foot before reaching the frontier, and eluded the pursuit of Indians and scores of Canadian militia. Old Samuel Edison and his second wife misled the searching parties sent to arrest him.

Samuel Edison presently arrived at Detroit and assisted in two more sallies against Canada. After these had failed he wandered round the shore of Lake Erie, seeking a new home. He decided to settle at Milan, a village on a canal connecting Lake Erie with the eastern cities. Before the Ohio railway system was built, as much as thirty-five thousand bushels of grain passed through Milan in one day. The village seemed to have the prospects of a Chicago.

Samuel Edison started a business in shingles. There was a large demand for them owing to the rapid building of houses. He called his family to Milan in 1839. He was soon able to establish them in a well-built brick house. Several more children were born and, in 1847, his son Thomas Alva Edison.

Samuel Edison was now forty-three, with a prosperous business and many children. He might have been expected to continue in this happy condition for the rest of his life. Unfortunately, new railroads destroyed the use of the canal and Milan declined. He had acquired some wealth, and in 1854 moved to a large house in Port Huron, at the southern end of Lake Huron. He became a dealer in grain and cattle-feed, and various other trades. There was a magnificent view of Lake Huron from his house, so he built an observation tower over one hundred feet high, from which the public could look out through a telescope, for a small charge.

Thomas Alva Edison spent his early childhood in this prosperous, changing, and beautiful environment.

The start of the Civil War provided Samuel Edison with another fine opportunity for opposing the majority. Though living in the far North, he publicly supported the South.

At the age of sixty, he easily could walk 63 miles from Port Huron to Detroit, and at nearly seventy he accomplished a jump approaching twenty feet from the side of a ship onto a quay. He died at about ninety years, and several of his sons, Thomas Alva Edison's brothers, lived over ninety years. His mother's grandfather was also reputed to have lived over a hundred years.

The inventor's paternal ancestors had exceptional physique and independent character, and his maternal ancestors were a professional family with more than the common education.

Endurance, obstinacy, and sense could not be unexpected in a child of these strains.

3

Edison played around the canal, the warehouses, and shipbuilding yards when he was an infant in Milan. He asked questions incessantly, and his demands for explanations of what seemed obvious to his elders created the belief that he was less than normally intelligent. As his head was abnormally large, it was thought that he might have a brain disease. He exhibited a good memory by learning the songs of the lumbermen and bargees before he was five years old. In old age he could remember having seen " prairie schooners," or covered wagons, at Milan when he was three or four years old, which had been prepared for the journey to the Californian goldfields.

A little later, he had an experience which may have left a strong psychological impression. He and another boy went to bathe in a creek. The other boy disappeared in the water. Edison waited for some time, and then went home, as darkness was falling. He did not say anything about the occurrence. Two hours later the disappearance was discovered, and he was asked about what happened. As he described the circumstances, he had a feeling of guilt, as if he were responsible. It is possible that the intensity of his work in later life may have been due partly to a desire to expiate this feeling of guilt.

Edison's education was conducted by his capable mother. He had attended a school for three months, but made no progress. An inspector described him as addled. He has stated that under his mother's direction he had read Gibbon's *Decline and Fall of the Roman Empire*, Hume's *History of England*, Burton's *Anatomy of Melancholy* and the *Dictionary of Sciences* before he was twelve, and together they had looked at Newton's *Principia*.

Edison's companions noticed that he showed surprising obedience when his mother called him in to take his lessons. At the age of ten or eleven he became interested in chemistry and experimenting. He had read a copy of Parker's *Natural and Experimental Philosophy*, a school textbook of physics and chemistry, or what would now be called " general science," at the age of nine, and presently tried many of the experiments described in it. He arranged a little laboratory in the cellar under the house. Like hundreds of other boys, he became deeply interested in the changes of matter, and the interactions of solids, liquids, and gases. In his later years Edison said that this aspect of things remained his deepest interest, and he was more of a chemist than physicist or engineer.

He made the usual collection of bottles, and odds and ends, for his cellar laboratory. He had two hundred bottles containing chemicals bought from the local drug store. He labelled all of them " poison." This action was rather unusual. If he had been prompted by a purely scientific motive, he would have labelled as " poison " only those bottles containing poison.

He probably labelled all because he wished to frighten off other children who threatened to interfere with his things, and also to impress outsiders with the danger and mystery of his activities. This command of bluff was an important element in his character, and assisted his future success.

As Edison did not attend school, owing to his reputed dullness and the belief that his constitution was delicate, he could spare much time for playing in his laboratory. He was not without pocket-money, which he spent on buying more chemicals, wire, copper, and zinc, for making voltaic batteries, etc.

In a period of construction such as existed in the Great Lakes district at that time, bits of metal, wood, stone, etc., were always lying about. There was a general atmosphere of constructive initiative. Nearly everyone was making some new thing, and used his own hands if he could not obtain more skilled help. Edison's father tried a variety of trades with a lively and amusing energy, and with sufficient success to provide his family with plenty of the ordinary domestic goods. The rapid change, and relative ease of acquisition, engendered open-handed habits. This helped Edison to get the things he wanted. In the settled European countries it was more difficult for a youth to get unusual things because the routine of life was more definite. A city such as London might contain more inspiring resources and personalities than an American township, but this was discounted by inaccessibility due to social stratification. What was the use of knowing, perhaps, that Sir William Thomson lived round the corner, if it was not possible to make his acquaintance? The smaller amount of social exclusiveness in American life in the middle of the nineteenth century assisted initiative. It was less probable that persons with ideas would fail because no one had heard of them.

Edison spent as much time as possible playing with his chemicals. He increased his pocket-money by doing odd jobs. At the age of eleven he drove a horse and wagon with vegetables from his father's market garden round the town, and sold $600 worth in a year. He also worked in the garden, but did not like it. He said afterwards that it was not surprising that humanity had invented city life, after experiencing the toil of hoeing under a hot sun. He sought for some more attractive way of earning money. At that date, boys of twelve usually worked. Schooling was casual, and his father probably did not consider it important. He went to work partly because it was customary and partly because he hoped to get more money to spend on chemicals and materials.

He fancied the task of selling newspapers and candy on the local railroads. He had much difficulty in persuading his mother to allow him to do this, but he received permission from her, and presently was at work on the trains between Port Huron and Detroit.

He was not sent to sell papers on trains, but started business as a newspaper salesman on his own initiative. He employed himself, and was virtually a member of the employing class from the age of twelve. Edison was not a poor boy who rose from the lowest social strata. He came from a family that had always produced leaders and employed a modest number of workmen, and he exhibited their psychology while he was a boy.

Edison began to do business on the trains in 1859, just before the Civil War started. His establishment in earnest work before the development of this crisis was of first-class importance. Unlike an inexperienced schoolboy, he was in contact with the contemporary working life, and in a position where he could receive directly the impulses of the forces released by the vast struggle between different social and economic classes.

The train for Detroit left Port Huron at 7 A.M., and arrived back in the evening at 9.30. He continued to sell papers in Port Huron until 11 P.M. As a child of twelve years, he had acquired the habit of working very long hours with little sleep. After he had been working on this train for a few months he opened two stores in Port Huron, one for periodicals and the other for vegetables and fruit in season. He appointed two other boys to attend them, and gave them a share in the profits. Then he engaged a boy to sell papers on the new Detroit express.

The express had a little-used United States mail, baggage and smoking car. He bought vegetables in Detroit markets which were superior to those in Port Huron, and put them in this car. No one asked him to pay freight. He said that he could never explain why, though perhaps it was because he was so small and industrious, and " the nerve to appropriate a U.S. mail-car to do a free freight business was so monumental." Edison's success in obtaining free facilities was due also to the unfinished organization of the railroad system. Between 1850 and 1860 the length of the United States railroads was extended from 7,500 miles to 30,000. Empty cars and small newsboys were easily overlooked in this immense development.

He bought butter along the line, and a large quantity of fruit in season. He bought wholesale at a low price, and allowed the wives of engineers and trainmen to buy at a discount.

He employed a boy to sell bread, tobacco, and candy on other trains. As the Civil War developed, he found the sales of daily newspapers became very profitable, so he closed down the vegetable store.

His businesses were relatively very profitable. He often made eight or ten dollars a day. He gave his mother one dollar a day for keep, and spent the rest on chemicals and apparatus.

The work on the train he served himself did not take all of his time, so he began to collect chemicals to play with on the way. The small smoking compartment was not used because it had no ventilation, so he turned it to his convenience. He brought many of his bottles and chemicals from the cellar at home and arranged them as a little laboratory. At quiet times on the runs between the stations, and no doubt during the halt in Detroit, he experimented.

As his train arrived in Detroit about 10 A.M. and left about 7 P.M., he spent about nine hours a day in the larger town. He read technical literature in a library, bought chemicals from the drug stores, and spent much time in the Grand Trunk Railroad machine shops, and other interesting places. Expensive materials were bought on the instalment plan. With several dollars a day to spend, he could afford even rare substances.

He became acquainted with Pullman, who at that time had a small shop in Detroit, and was experimenting with his sleeping-car. Pullman made wooden chemical apparatus for him. Edison studied Fresenius' *Qualitative Analysis*, and tried the tests in his train-laboratory.

The stimulation of newspaper sales by the Civil War impressed Edison with the business possibilities of news. He decided to found his own paper. He bought a small press that had been used for printing hotel menus. This was kept at home, but on the train he had some supplies of type, so he could compose in spare moments. He named his paper the *Weekly Herald*. He sold it at three cents per copy, or eight cents per month to regular subscribers, and the sales of an issue sometimes exceeded four hundred copies.

The *Weekly Herald* was probably the first newspaper in the world to be published on a train. It was noticed by the London *Times*, and by Robert Stephenson when he inspected the Grand Trunk Railroad.

It contained boosts of friendly engine-drivers, or engineers, market prices, new train and road services, police and military news, and advertisements of his own businesses. In one issue there was an announcement under the " Birth " heading :

" At Detroit Junction G.T.R. Refreshment Rooms on the 29th inst, the wife of A. Little of a daughter."

Lower down the column, as a fill-up, he inserted :

" Reason, Justice and Equity, never had weight enough on the face of the earth, to govern the councils of men."

He recommended Mr. E. L. Northrop to the railroad direction as " being the most steady driver we have ever rode behind (and we consider ourselves some judge, haveing been Railway riding for over two years constantly)." Mr. Northrop was " always kind, and obligeing, and ever at his post. His Engine we understand does not cost one-fourth for repairs what the other Engines do." Perhaps Mr. Northrop was the engineer who sometimes allowed Edison to drive the train engine.

When he arrived by his train at Detroit one day in April, 1862, he found the newspaper offices surrounded by excited crowds reading bulletins of the battle of Shiloh. The Confederate armies had received several defeats in Kentucky and Tennessee, in the western area of the war.

Their commander, Johnston, received an indirect reprimand from his old friend Jefferson Davis, which prompted him to start an offensive campaign which might retrieve all that had been lost, and gain still more. The Northern forces of Sherman and Grant were situated near a log meeting-house called Shiloh, between two creeks running into the Tennessee River. A large part of the Northern troops were raw, and had learnt the elements of military drill only on the way to the front. Grant judged that learning some technique and discipline was more important than erecting fortifications. Johnston attempted to drive the Northern armies into the river and creeks. His troops attacked fiercely and many men on both sides soon retreated in panic. Grant saw four or five thousand panic-stricken Northern troops lying under the river bluff, who could have been shot without resistance. Similar disorder occurred at the rear of the Confederate army.

About five thousand soldiers were killed and twenty thousand wounded in this battle.

Grant writes that until the battle of Shiloh, he and thousands of other citizens believed the secession movement would collapse after a decisive victory over any of its armies. But when, after that battle, the Confederates were seen to be preparing yet another line and offensive, he no longer expected that the Union would be saved without complete conquest. Up to that time, the Northern armies had protected the property of citizens in invaded territory, irrespective of their sentiments, but afterwards Grant " regarded it as humane to both sides to protect the persons of those found at their homes, but to consume everything that could be used to support or supply armies."

The battle of Shiloh was the most ferocious fought in the West. The general conception of the Civil War changed after it, and became more profound and ruthless. Many soldiers and citizens had regarded the war largely as a sporting contest, in which men from the North and South fought duels in battalions instead of pairs.

The first accounts of Shiloh which reached Detroit stated there had been 60,000 casualties. As the crowds, and Edison, stared at the newspaper bulletins, they acquired new insight into the seriousness of the war, and became more aware of the depth of the forces moving under the struggle.

Edison perceived that everyone would be anxious to read accounts of the battle, and there should be a large increase in the demand for newspapers.

" I then conceived the idea of telegraphing the news ahead, went to the operator in the depot, and by giving him *Harper's Weekly* and some other papers for three months, he agreed to telegraph to all the stations the matter on the bulletin-board."

He decided that he would need a thousand, instead of the usual hundred, copies of the Detroit newspaper. He had not enough money to purchase that number, so he determined in desperation to see the editor and get credit. He went into the editorial office and found two men in charge, one of whom, after the telegraphing scheme had been explained, said he could take the thousand copies. With the help of another boy, he lugged the papers to the train. The first stop was at Utica, where he usually sold two papers. He saw a crowd ahead at the station, and thought it some excursion, " but the moment I landed there was a rush for me ; then I realized that the telegraph was a great invention."

The next stop was at Mount Clemens. Between the stations he decided to raise the price of the paper from five to ten cents, if there was a crowd. His expectation proved to be correct.

Edison used to jump off the train about a quarter of a mile outside Port Huron station. He had deposited some loads of sand at the place, in order to form a soft landing place. He was met here by a Dutch boy with a horse and wagon. On this occasion, the boys found a large crowd waiting for them as they entered the outskirts of the town.

" I then yelled : ' Twenty-five cents apiece, gentlemen ! I haven't enough to go round ! ' I sold all out, and made what to me then was an immense sum of money."

Some time afterwards his train laboratory was abolished through an accident. Some phosphorus was jolted onto the floor, and set fire to the car. The conductor put the fire out, but he turned Edison and his bottles and the printing type out of the train at the next station.

He continued printing his paper at home, but presently converted it into a gossip sheet, and changed its title to *Paul Pry*. Personal remarks in the paper provoked an enraged reader into throwing Edison into the St. Clair River.

If Edison had wished, he could have become a master of tabloid journalism.

Edison's experience of social types is illustrated by his account of an experience on his train in 1860, just before the Civil War started. Two fine-looking young men, with a coloured servant, boarded the train one afternoon at Detroit for Port Huron. Edison presently came round to offer them evening papers. One of them said to him : " Boy, what have you got ? '" " I said : ' Papers.' ' All right.' He took them and threw them out of the window, and, turning to the coloured man, said : ' Nicodemus, pay this boy.' I told Nicodemus the amount, and he opened a satchel and paid me. The passengers did not know what to make of the transaction. I returned with the illustrated papers and magazines. These were seized and thrown out of the window, and I was told to get my money of Nicodemus. I then returned with all the old magazines and novels I had not been able to sell, thinking perhaps this would be too much for them. I was small and thin, and the layer reached above my head, and was all I could possibly carry. I had prepared a list, and knew the amount in case they bit again. When I opened the door, all the passengers roared with laughter. I walked right up to the young men. I said : ' Magazines and novels.' He promptly threw them out of the window, and Nicodemus settled. Then I came in with cracked hickory nuts, then pop-corn balls, and, finally, molasses candy. All went out of the window. I felt like Alexander the Great !—I had no more chance ! Finally I put a rope to my trunk, which was about the size of a carpenter's chest, and started to pull this from the baggage-car to the passenger-car. It was almost too much for my strength, but at last I got it in front of those men. I pulled off my coat, shoes, and hat, and laid them on the chest. Then he asked : ' What have you got, boy ? ' I said : ' Everything, sir, that I can spare that is for sale.' The passengers fairly jumped with laughter. Nicodemus paid me $27 for this last sale, and threw the whole out of the door in the rear of the car. These men were from the South, and I have always retained a soft spot in my heart for a Southern gentleman."

Perhaps the perfection of this story grew with the years, but it provides an artistic expression of differences in social class and ideals between the North and South.

Edison's father said that his son never had any boyhood of the usual sort. There was no period of adolescent irresponsibility.

Edison became deaf through an accident on the railroad. He said that he was waiting for some newspaper customers, when the train started. He ran after it, and had some difficulty in clambering on. A trainman reached down and grabbed him by the ears and hauled him into safety. Edison felt something crack in his ears, and afterwards he grew deaf. He said that if the trainman had damaged his hearing, he had also saved his life.

Edison has said that he became deeply interested in electricity while on the railroad, through his acquaintance with telegraphers and telegraph offices. He already knew something about the theory of the telegraph, as his textbook by Parker contained a short account of Morse's system. With his knowledge of chemistry and mechanics he constructed rough telegraphs, and learned the Morse signalling code. This was not remarkable, as hundreds of boys were playing with the telegraph at that time. The invention was still new. It appealed to the desire for power, and the ability to exert power at a distance. One reason why guns are fascinating is that they exert effects at a distance, and extend the feeling of human power. The telegraph allowed orders to be given almost instantaneously. It satisfied the primitive desire for superhuman power, or magic. This universal feeling had the first place in the motives of Edison's hundreds of young contemporary experimenters. But Edison had another motive. He had found by experience that " the telegraph was a great invention " because it had enabled him to make a relatively large sum of money. It was great because, in addition to its ingenuity, it had immense economic power. The recognition of this by a boy of fourteen, on the basis of personal test, was exceptional.

The first successful telegraph depending on electro-magnets was devised in America by Henry. Cooke and Wheatstone devised a telegraph, based on the results of Henry's researches, in England in 1837, and its practical value was first demonstrated through its assistance in de-taining a murderer who was escaping by train into London. It happened that the telegraph had been set up as a demon-stration unit at the station where the murderer boarded the train. A description of the man was sent to London, and he was arrested as he got off the train. Before that event, the unit was regarded by the railway authorities and the public as an amusing toy.

A more convenient form of telegraph was invented by S. F. B. Morse, an American painter. Morse went to Europe to improve his mastery of his art, and after four years' work, returned to America in 1832. He happened to meet on his ship fellow-passengers who were keenly interested in recent progress in the knowledge of electricity. During discussions with them, he conceived the possibility of com-munication by electricity, and he began to think how it might be accomplished. Like Leonardo he was able to apply skill in drawing to the design of mechanisms, and soon made some beautiful sketches. He gradually worked out a practical method, though he was not an engineer or scientist.

The creation of the practical electric telegraph by Cooke and Wheatstone, and Morse, was not done quickly. They worked persistently, under the pressure of the social and economic importance of their aim. The railroads could not be developed extensively without swift communication for the control of traffic. Railroad and telegraph grew together. These methods of transport and communication were ex-ceptionally important in America because distances were so great.

The extension of the railroad and telegraph between 1840 and 1860 vastly increased the unification of the United States. Before that period the states could without excessive friction enjoy " states' rights " because the communications between states were so bad. After 1840 the states were brought into much closer contact, and could not avoid taking detailed notice of the practices of their neighbours. For instance, it increased the difficulty of the problem of the restoration of escaped slaves. A negro slave in a Southern state was a piece of personal property. If he ran away, he had to be restored by his finder, like any other piece of lost property. Before the railroad was introduced an escaped slave could not usually go very far, owing to the cost and difficulty of transport, but afterwards he might travel thousands of miles by jumping on freight trains. The railroad increased the number of escaped slaves in the North, and set the problem of slavery with awkward concreteness in front of the Northern population. The introduction of the telegraph exacerbated the problem, because it could be used for helping to catch escaped slaves.

Improved communications made the United States much smaller, as they have since contracted the effective social size of the whole earth. They were brought forth by industrialism, fundamentally as means to increase trade. They grew much faster in the Northern states because they are more important to communities trading in manufactured goods, which need quicker transport than those trading in raw materials. Manufactured goods are far more valuable than raw materials, bulk for bulk. Northern traders enthusiastically pulled the whole of the United States together with rails and wires, in order to assist business, and presently discovered that the closer contact had exposed the incompatibility of the interests of the governing classes in the North and South. The former wanted the United States to be turned into an efficient organization, surrounded by a high tariff fence, for absorbing goods and producing profits, whereas the latter wanted security in slave property and free trade for increasing the export of raw materials. Neither class objected to slavery.

The power of the governing classes of the North and South was evenly balanced about 1850. After that date, the North became stronger, owing to the greater inherent possibilities of economic power in industrial capitalism, and to important changes in political circumstances, several of which were due to the railroad and telegraph.

Small farmers and tradesmen constituted a large part of the Northern population. In spite of their numbers, they had less influence than the rich on the direction of Northern growth and the formulation of Northern ideals. In the 1850's the Northern rich decided that the small farmers and traders might be engaged as allies in the fight against the Southern rich, through their fear of the extension of slavery. The small men found that the railroad and telegraph had

brought slaves and the search for slaves into their own terri-
tories. They feared the introduction of slave competition,
and they began to dislike the principle of slavery.

The Republican Party was formed to combine the Northern
capitalists and small men in the struggle against the Southern
slave-owning planters. The aims of the two wings of the party
were profoundly different. The capitalists were on the offensive and wished to control the South in their own interests.
They did not object to slavery.

Morse, whose invention had done so much to assist the
growth of industrialism, and to unify America in industrial
interests, was an ardent supporter of slavery, which he
justified by appeals to the Bible ; and an equally ardent
opponent of secession. His views agreed with those of New
York bankers. He became the president of a Society for the
Diffusion of Political Knowledge which was anti-war, pro-
union, and pro-slavery ; and was supported by a number of
millionaires. Morse was extremely sincere and hated the
hypocrisy of the slavery abolitionists. He based his arguments on what appeared to him as the highest religious truths.
He believed abolition was " the logical progeny of Uni-
tarianism and Infidelity." But his principles were in effect
those of the Northern capitalists, who desired the preservation
of the Union for the sake of efficiency, and no interference with
slavery in order to preserve the sanctity of private property.

A purely capitalist policy was not possible, partly because
of his own invention. The telegraph had helped to put the
small men on the defensive, against the introduction of
slavery which would undermine their personal positions.

They gained temporary political power through their
defensive movement. The Northern capitalists were forced
to compromise with them and form the new Republican
Party, and accept their nominee, Abraham Lincoln, the former
backwoodsman, as leader. The less subtle supporters of
policies equivalent in practice with those of the pure capitalists,
fiercely opposed Lincoln. At Lincoln's second candidature
they nominated McClellan in opposition. McClellan was
introduced at his biggest New York rally by Morse, who lent
him his arm to lead him before the audience.

When Edison became acquainted with the telegraph it
was the young nerve of the growing social giant of American
industrialism. It attracted the courageous inventors and
operators, who, today, would be interested in aeronautics
and radio. It has been said that the telephone, which was

the offspring of the telegraph, was "the little mother of the big trust." The servants of the early telegraph felt immense potentialities as they sent messages with triumphant instantaneity from state to state across a continent. Edison had already learned by experience that a corner in news could be arranged through the telegraph. He desired to become a professional telegrapher. This was not very easy, because the practice necessary for proficiency could not be obtained outside a telegraph office. Again he found his chance on the railroad. One day in August, 1862, his train was shunting at an intermediate station. He happened to see the infant son of the station agent playing on the line in front of a car which had just been shunted. He ran to the child and carried him out of the way of the approaching car. The grateful father was glad to reward Edison by teaching him train telegraphy.

Edison practised in the agent's office for several months, sometimes for eighteen hours a day. He made his own set of telegraph instruments in a gun-shop in Detroit. After he had acquired some proficiency, he attempted to start his own telegraph business. He erected a wire between the station and the village, which were about a mile apart, and hoped to make a living by sending messages over this short distance. He was disappointed, as no one wished to use a telegraph over a distance of one mile, so he was forced to seek employment as a company telegrapher. His attempt to start his own business before seeking employment by others was characteristic. He was assisted in finding a job by the Civil War. The telegrapher at Port Huron wished to enlist in the highly-paid United States Military Telegraph Corps, so he recommended Edison for his own job. Edison was fifteen years old. He used to work all day in the office, and then until 3 A.M., in order to practise the taking of press reports, which was the most difficult and highly-paid telegraphic work. Presently he obtained a post as night telegrapher on the Grand Trunk Railroad at Stratford in Canada. This was not far from the Edisons' old Canadian home.

Edison was not a very conscientious employee. He read scientific books and experimented with the instruments. He put on one side telegrams handed to him for dispatch, until he could conveniently interrupt his studies. He showed similar insensitiveness in borrowing other people's valuable tools. While at Stratford he heard of the existence of boxes of old batteries at another station. He asked the operator there whether he might have them, and was told that he could. The batteries consisted of eighty Grove cells, with electrodes which contained altogether several ounces of platinum. He was delighted with this acquisition, and still was using some of the platinum in his laboratory forty years later. He made his first invention at Stratford, when he was sixteen years old. Night operators were required to send hourly signals to show they were awake. He devised a clock which made the time signals automatically. This enabled him to sleep while on duty, and preserve his energy for his own interests during the daytime. He was presently found out and reprimanded. His automatic timing device was similar in principle to the apparatus introduced for calling district messengers from a central office.

Edison's job at Stratford ended through a misunderstanding over the signalling of two trains. They were allowed to run off towards each other on the same track, and a collision was averted only through the promptitude of the engine-drivers, who could see each other's trains at a distance on the straight track. Edison was called to Toronto to explain the affair. His examination by the general manager was interrupted by two English visitors, and while he was waiting, he decided to run away. He returned to Michigan and got a job as operator on the railroad at Adrian. He was discharged owing to the misunderstanding between two superintendents who had given him contradictory orders. As they were friends, they laid the blame on him. He had no difficulty in obtaining another job, as the Civil War in this year, 1863, had fully developed. The Federal army had absorbed fifteen hundred operators, besides a few hundred who had enlisted as soldiers, so anyone with the roughest proficiency could secure a civilian job. Edison wandered over the central states from Detroit to New Orleans during the next five years. He became a member of the class of tramp operators which has a special place in American history. The shortage during the Civil War, and in the years of swift reconstruction and expansion afterwards, conferred a high degree of freedom on operators. If they disliked their superiors they could tell them what they thought of them, and often retain their jobs, or immediately get another elsewhere. Trade-unionism was strong among them. They could travel free over the whole country, as the railroad men regarded them as colleagues, owing to the close connection between railroad and telegraph.

The operator's work, with the rough instruments of the time, required considerable skill, so the operators were brighter than the average man. Their contact with the news tended to keep them intellectually alert.

Such circumstances helped to maintain the high standard of freedom and intelligence among the operators, but others destroyed good habits. Many operators suffered from the strain of heavy telegraphing, and drank to relieve their nerves. As the rates of pay were high they could indulge in wild debaucheries, and as jobs were easy to get, sacking did not deter them. The drifting from place to place interfered with marriage.

Edison lived with such colleagues for five years, between the ages of sixteen and twenty-one, from 1863 to 1868. The living conditions during the war period were rough, and after the war, when the military telegraphers returned, were even wilder. The operators added handiness with guns to their other aberrations. They had lost much of even such routine as civilian operators possessed.

Edison obtained a post with the Western Union Telegraph Company in 1864 at Indianapolis. He left this post possibly owing to trouble over another invention. He had not yet learned to take press reports very quickly, so he devised an instrument which would take the messages as they came in, and then repeat them at a slower speed. He could write out the messages in beautiful copy with this assistance, without delay when the rate of business was normal, but at rush hours he was left behind. The newspaper offices complained of the slowness with which they received their copy. Edison's repeater consisted of a disc of paper which received the signal indentations along a volute spiral. He said later that this instrument helped him to conceive the phonograph while working on the development of the telephone.

Edison moved on to Cincinnati. A fellow telegrapher, M. F. Adams, has described Edison's appearance when he drifted in there for a job. He was badly dressed, and his manners were uncouth. He was thin, and his nose was prominent. He was unpopular, but had no superiors as an operator. He was always playing with the batteries and circuits, and trying to make telegraphy less irksome. He played jokes on his colleagues by making their instruments function abnormally, and arranged special circuits for electrocuting some of the rats which infested the offices.

Edison was in the Cincinnati office when the account of

Lincoln's assassination went through. The operator who took the press report was working so mechanically that he did not take in its sense. The telegraph office.first learned the news from the newspaper office which had received their report.

Edison often went to the theatre at Cincinnati. He was particularly fond of *Othello*. He increased his earnings by copying plays for the theatre.

He was promoted into the most highly paid grade of operators, apparently, judging from his own account published by Dyer and Martin, through willingness to blackleg on other operators absent in connection with their union. At any rate, he seems to have been in the office when his unionist colleagues were out.

Soon afterwards he moved to Memphis in Tennessee, where the telegraph was still under military control just after the Civil War. Edison says that he devised a repeater which enabled him to connect New York and New Orleans for the first time after the war. The superintendent was also working on repeaters, and discharged him through jealousy. Edison nearly starved in Alabama, and arrived in Louisville on an icy day, wearing a linen duster suit.

Many of the operators who returned after the war found civilian life too boring. Edison describes how colleagues used to throw ink around the office, and pistol cartridges into the fire.

" Everything at that time was ' wide open.' Disorganization reigned supreme. There was no head or anything. At night myself and a.companion would go over to a gorgeously furnished faro-bank and get our midnight lunch. Everything was free. There were over twenty keno-rooms running. One of them that I visited was in a Baptist church, the man with the wheel being in the pulpit, and the gamblers in the pews."

Edison describes how, while he was in Cincinnati during the Civil War, he had to pass on an urgent cipher message from the War Office in Washington to General Thomas at Nashville, who was threatened by the Confederate General Hood. The connection to Nashville went through Louisville, so Edison tried to call the Louisville office, but could not get any reply. After much trouble a roundabout telegraph connection was made through the Indianapolis-Louisville railroad. Inquiry showed that the silent Louisville office should have been served by three operators, but one of them had fallen off his horse and broken his leg, another had been knifed in a keno-room, and the third had gone to Cynthiana to see a man hanged and had missed the return train.

Edison stayed in Louisville for the long period of two years. He had to serve a wire that passed through a badly insulated cable under the River Ohio. This and other defects rendered accurate reception difficult. He frequently had to guess at unintelligible noises. He found he could not write quickly enough to leave time for the working of his imagination, so he began to experiment with different scripts. He evolved an efficient vertical style with simplified separate letters, of a sort which has since been much recommended by educational psychologists to ease the learning of writing by school children. Edison's script was evolved in 1865, and is a beautiful example of functionalist design.

I think the most important line of 'investigation' is the production of Electricity direct from carbon.

Edison

Edison's Handwriting

The telegraph room at Louisville had lost one-third of the plaster from its ceiling. It was never cleaned. The switchboard was about thirty-four inches square. Its brass connections were corroded with age, and sparking from lightning flashes. According to Edison " it would strike on the wires with an explosion like a cannon-shot." The copper connecting wires were crystallized and rotten, and the fumes from the nitric acid battery had eaten away the woodwork in the battery room. One night a drunken operator came in and kicked the stove over, tore the switchboard off the wall, and then went to the battery room and knocked the batteries onto the floor. The escaping acid percolated through the floor and destroyed account-books in the room underneath. Edison left the wreckage as it stood, for the manager's inspection. He rigged up a temporary set of instruments. When the manager came in, he asked Edison who had done it. " I told him that Billy L. had come in full of soda water and invented the ruin before him. He walked backward and forward, about a minute, then coming up to my table put his fist down, and said : ' If Billy L. ever does that again, I will discharge him.' "

Such was the influence of the shortage of labour at this time.

Edison wandered back to Detroit, and then to New Orleans with the intention of emigrating to South America with two companions. He was advised by an acquaintance in New Orleans not to go, so he presently returned to operating in Louisville and Cincinnati. He became acquainted with a brilliant operator named Ellsworth, who could imitate the transmitting styles of other operators. Ellsworth had fought with the Confederates, and had caused much confusion among the Federalists by tapping their wires and sending false messages over them. Ellsworth suggested that Edison should invent a method of sending dispatches which could not be intercepted, as he could obtain a high price for it from the Government. Edison said that he evolved the germ of his quadruplex system of telegraphy, by which four messages may be sent simultaneously over one wire, in his attempts to solve the problem Ellsworth had set him. Ellsworth presently disappeared, as he could not settle down after the war. He became a gunman in the Panhandle of Texas. After he had gone, Edison dropped the research.

Edison returned to his home at Port Huron in 1868. He soon became unhappy without work, so he wrote to his old operator friend M. F. Adams, who was at Boston, asking if he knew of a job. Adams showed a sample of his copy to the superintendent of the Western Union office, who was favourably impressed. Edison left for Boston, but his train was delayed by a blizzard, and arrived at Montreal several days late. An operator put him up there in the most cheerless boarding house he had ever seen. The food was inadequate, the bedclothes were short and thin, the temperature was 28 degrees below zero, and the water was frozen solid in the jug. " The usual livestock accompaniment of operators' boarding houses was absent," probably owing to the intense cold.

When he presented himself at the Boston office he looked raw, even as a pioneering American of 1868. His trousers were too small and light, his shoes were worn out, his butternut hat from the South was dilapidated, and he wore his hair in the cowlick style. His accent was uncultivated, as it remained through his life, he chewed tobacco, and spat copiously. The five years of wandering had assimilated his manners to the rougher part of the wild society in which he had lived. He had not acquired suavity by travel. But he had not been destroyed. He was not seduced from continual experimenting and reading by any environment. He fairly regularly sacrificed his employer's interests to his own. His successful self-control through these interesting but dangerous years was due mainly to the cast of his character, but was assisted by his deafness. This ailment made telegraph work harder, as a large part of reception at that time consisted of taking messages from a ticker by ear. There was also a benefit in deafness, as he was not distracted by the noise of instruments in other parts of the room. Perhaps the extra listening effort, which Edison had to make, increased self-control in other directions.

The deafness must have interfered with social life. It probably helped to separate him from dissolute companions, and fostered isolated studiousness, as it often does. His deafness increased his insensitivity to his surroundings, and allowed him to work and think in conditions which would have distracted many men. It strengthened the naturally strong individualistic, egoistic disposition he had inherited from his obstinate ancestors.

The Boston operators decided to " put a job on the jay from the woolly West." As his first assignment he was put onto one of the most difficult wires, and presently was told to take a special report for the Boston *Herald.* The Boston operators had arranged with New York to have it sent by one of their fastest senders. Edison sat down and began to take down the report, which came through slowly at first, and then with increasing speed. Through his special script he was able to write faster than any sender could send, so he kept up easily. On looking up, he noticed that the operators were watching him, and he guessed what they were doing. The sender began to slur words, abbreviate, and use other tricks, but Edison was accustomed to them. After a time, he took his own key, and '" remarked, telegraphically, to my New York friend : ' Say, young man, change off and send with your other foot.' " The New York man dropped the joke after that, and turned the sending over to another man.

At Boston, as usual, Edison put his own interests first. He avoided the press telegraphy and chose the ordinary work because the free intervals between casual business could be used for reading and experimenting.

He was not the employer's ideal of a workman. If all American workmen had behaved with Edison's determined self-interestedness, the history of American industry would have been stormier.

He found and bought a set of Faraday's works in Boston. He said that he learned more from these books than from any others. He tried the experiments Faraday described, and he appreciated his simple, non-mathematical explanations. He considered Faraday the Master Experimenter. Edison said that not many of Faraday's works were sold in America at that time. Few people did anything in electricity, except telegraphers, and opticians who made simple apparatus for school science classes.

Edison became familiar with Charles Williams' factory in Boston for the manufacture of telegraph apparatus. Williams afterwards became the first manufacturer of telephones, in association with Bell. One of his men helped Edison with the construction of the model for his first patented invention. This was an apparatus for quickly recording votes in the House of Representatives. Electric buttons were to be placed on members' desks, so that votes could be registered without calling the roll of members' names, and walking into particular lobbies.

The idea and arrangement were simple. Edison thought the apparatus would be attractive because it would save much legislative time, but when he demonstrated it before the politicians in Washington, they explained that it would be unwelcome, because it would destroy the system of obstructing parliamentary business by calling for votes or divisions, each of which wasted time.

After this experience Edison decided to let the market set him his inventive work. He would not attempt inventions of value to humanity unless there was a definite market for them. This decision was historically important. Edison was the first great scientific inventor who clearly conceived invention as subordinate to commerce. He abandoned the traditional theory that inventions and discoveries are independent creations, having no necessary connection with other affairs. According to the traditional theory they are the products of pure thought. The moment at which they came into existence is supposed to depend only on the presence of a particular genius. It is assumed that if Isaac Newton had lived in China two thousand years ago, he would have presented the Chinese with the laws of gravitation. The traditional explanation of why the laws of gravitation were discovered in the seventeenth century is that Newton happened to be born then. As Pope wrote :

God said : Let Newton be, and all was light.

According to this view, the light of gravitation would have been seen in 1665 B.C. instead of A.D. 1665, if God had chosen to let Newton be twenty-three years of age on the former date.

The old theory that inventions and discoveries are due solely to genius contains some truth, but more error. When stated boldly today it seems fantastically erroneous, as the contemporary mind has more sense of history than its predecessors. The notion that inventions come into existence through unaccountable acts of creation has become as unacceptable now as the Genesis story of the Creation, after Darwin had established the theory of evolution, in the nineteenth century.

It preserves its authority because it contains a fraction of truth, and because historians of science and invention have done so little towards working out a better theory. The sole generally known fact is that inventions and discoveries are produced by clever persons. The obvious connection between cleverness and invention has inspired the theory that invention is solely due to cleverness. But the clever person is only a small fraction of the phenomenon of invention. Important inventions are nearly always produced more or less simultaneously by several men, as the legal battles over patents prove. Cleverness probably does not contribute a twentieth part to any invention or discovery. The planet on which the inventor lives is one factor. The century and the country in which he lives, his social class and family, are other factors.

After these and others have been allowed for, the contribution of mere cleverness in invention does not appear overwhelming.

Edison's view that invention should be subordinate to commerce was an important advance in sociology. It made the way for the further advance to the conception of invention as a social product, with social responsibilities.

So long as invention was conceived as intellectual magic, it could not make an adequate contribution to human progress. After it had been made a servant of commerce, it could begin to evolve into a servant of humanity. It had to be made a servant of capitalism in order to acquire its correct position in future human societies.

Edison's career of invention has often been justified by fanciful estimates of the billions of dollars of wealth created through his work. These estimates have little meaning because it is impossible to disentangle Edison's part from those of others in the creation of this wealth. Some time ago it was estimated that Edison's inventions had brought into existence $10,300,000,000 of wealth in the United States alone. It would be more true to say that Edison's inventions had been brought into existence by $10,300,000,000. The potentiality of this wealth in the America of the nineteenth century created Edison far more than he created it.

When he decided to make inventions only for commercial demand, and not for the prestige of virtuosity, he admitted that that commercial demand, that potential $10,000,000,000, was the controller of his inspiration. He admitted the priority of commercial demand, so he renounced the priority of invention to wealth.

The traditional theory of invention is based on the notion of magic and superhuman power. In primitive society the clever man is supposed to have an element of divinity that places him above, and gives him rights over, other men. The conscious aim of much scholarship, scientific research, and invention is to qualify for this upper class of supermen, and enjoy its privileges and prestige. It is in the interest of members of this class to magnify the importance of cleverness in invention, because the amount of prestige is determined by the amount of magic. If the invention is very ingenious, the inventor is a great magician and entitled to great prestige. The more useless the invention, the greater its magic. Invention and discovery on the traditional theory are supposed to be merely pure acts of disinterested intelligence because such acts are the best qualification for entering the magical upper class, or leisure class, in Veblen's phrase.

Edison wrested invention from the magicians of the leisure class. He destroyed the illusion that inventors owe everything to their own cleverness.

The belief that innate qualities confer privileges is an essential part of the theory of aristocracy. When Edison undermined the prestige of the undirected inventive inspiration of the inventor who was merely clever, irrespective of the sociological value of his invention, he began to destroy the aristocratic elements in the traditional theory of invention. He began the advance towards a democratic theory in which invention would be cultivated in order to increase human happiness, rather than personal privileges. He did not suggest such a theory, but he abandoned the old theory, and thus made the approach possible.

At Boston Edison changed from a telegrapher interested in trying new arrangements with his apparatus, and studying science, into an inventor. He was twenty-one years old, and as he grew out of adolescence he immediately became a weightier personality.

After he patented his vote recorder, he invented a stock-ticker, for registering stock exchange quotations in any place by telegraph. The first stock-ticker had been introduced by Callahan in New York in 1867. It did not involve any major invention, but had to print stocks and prices in brokers' offices conveniently and reliably. A simplified form of printing tele-graph (first invented by D. E. Hughes in 1855) which could be installed in each broker's office, and operated from a central office in the stock exchange, was required.

Edison installed his stock-ticker in about thirty offices in Boston, but it was clear that New York, the chief centre of speculation, was by far the best place for development. He visited New York in 1868, to attempt to sell his stock-ticker, but failed, and returned to Boston.

He had many occupations in Boston. He put up telegraph lines between private business offices, fitted with simple alphabetical dial instruments, by which unskilled clerks could exchange messages. Edison says they slung wires over the house tops without asking anyone's permission. Apparently they went to houses and stores which already had wires sup-ported by the roofs, and told the occupants they were telegraph men and wanted to see the wires. They were always given permission to go up to them, and while there fastened up their own. This, apparently, is how it was possible for Edison, without capital, to put up his own small centralized telegraph system in the centre of a city. He did not pay rent for wires slung over the property of others.

He also worked on duplex telegraphy in Boston, in 1868.

This consists of sending two messages over one wire simultaneously in opposite directions. The duplex apparatus which first achieved commercial success was worked out in the same year in Boston by J. B. Stearns. Edison demonstrated his apparatus at Rochester, but without success, owing, he says, to lack of competent assistance.

Edison was now absorbed in invention. He had accumulated large debts through borrowing money for experiment and construction. He decided to go to New York, as development and success seemed more possible in the great commercial city. He arrived there in 1869, nearly starving. He begged tea from a tea-taster whom he saw at work in a warehouse, and borrowed one dollar from an operator friend who was himself out of work. He considered carefully the best value that could be had in food, and chose apple dumplings and coffee for his first lunch.

He applied for a post as operator with the Western Union, and slept at night in the battery room of the Gold Indicator Company. While waiting for instructions from the Western Union he studied the instruments of the Gold Indicator Company, who had their own system of tickers for telegraphing the variations in the price of gold to brokers and speculators. Edison had designed and introduced his own system in Boston. It was probably rougher and more amateurish than the New York system, and for those reasons had not been a commercial success. But Edison understood the principles thoroughly, so he could examine the New York equipment with professional interest. He mastered its details in a few days. This enabled him to profit from a development in the history of the United States, which became particularly prominent in 1869.

Hamilton and Madison, as the spokesmen of the rich, had conferred on the United States a constitution well adapted to their interests. The two chief features of the Constitution were the sanctity of human liberty and of private property. The Civil War was essentially an explicit struggle for power between two different classes of property owners, the Southern land and slave owners, and the Northern industrial capitalists. By winning the war the Northern money-owners established the precedence of their form of property. The Constitution was interpreted as sanctifying human liberty, and private property especially in industrial capital. The liberty of Americans was sacred, wealth was sacred, and rich Americans were therefore doubly sacred.

In this climate of beliefs millionaires appeared to have a quality not possessed by other men, which made them seem slightly superhuman. The reaction against this view, and the social forces it expressed, had made some progress before the end of the century, when the awe of millionaires began to decline.

The growth of the ascendancy of the millionaire, and the evolution of a form of society in which he was dominant, was naturally easy in such a richly endowed country as the United States. Very rich men had appeared in the United States before the Civil War, but they appeared in far greater profusion after. The financing of the Civil War had stimulated the natural habits of Americans to think in millions. The Northern finances were managed by Jay Cooke, who raised the size of financial operations to a new degree. Vast quantities of paper money were created to meet war loans, and pay bonuses to soldiers. This became material for speculation by hundreds of thousands of persons who would not have dreamt of speculating before the war. Similar phenomena occurred after the war of 1914–1918.

As liberty and money were generally felt to be sacred, there appeared to be no way of controlling them. They were above the law. Millionaires, as free Americans and rich men, did as they liked, and the community could not see how they could be controlled. After the Civil War the circumstances enabled millionaires to speculate on a higher scale than ever before. They played with the wealth of America as they wished, except for such interferences as arose from collisions among themselves. The railroads formed a considerable fraction of the new wealth that had been created in America. They included not only their own expensive equipment of tracks and rolling stock, but enormous estates granted to them by the Federal Government. The millionaires who controlled railroad finance were among the richest and most powerful. Naturally they were prominent in the post-war financial campaigns.

The possibilities of the situation inspired some of them to new visions of financial power. In 1866 Drew, as treasurer of the Erie Railway Company, had devised a way of transferring a large part of the wealth belonging to the shareholders in the company from them to himself. The position as a servant of a company, appointed to advance the interests of the shareholders, had never been so successfully abused before. As C. F. Adams, Jr., in his classical account of this and the succeeding events, wrote : " Mr. Drew was looked upon as having effected a surprisingly clever operation, and he retired from the field hated, feared, wealthy, and admired."

Shortly afterwards, in 1868, Cornelius Vanderbilt, popularly known as the Commodore, conceived a far grander style of operation in railroad finance. He aimed at acquiring control of all the railroads serving New York, so that he would have dictatorial power over all the trade with that city, and a large part of the trade of the United States. C. F. Adams, Jr., observed in 1869 that by combining the power of the individual with the power of the financial corporation, he had introduced Cæsarism into corporate life. " He has, however, but pointed out the way which others will tread. The individual will hereafter be engrafted on the corporation,—democracy running its course, and resulting in imperialism ; and Vanderbilt is but the precursor of a class of men who will wield within the state a power created by the state, but too great for its control. He is the founder of a dynasty."

By 1868 Vanderbilt had secured control of all the railroads serving New York, except the Erie, controlled by Drew. He now began a financial battle with Drew for the control of the Erie railroad.

" The cast of Drew's mind was sombre and bearish, Vanderbilt was gay and buoyant of temperament, little given to thoughts other than of this world, a lover of horses and of the good things of this life. The first affects prayer meetings, and the last is a devotee of whist. Drew, in Wall Street, is by temperament a bear, while Vanderbilt could hardly be other than a bull."

Vanderbilt was the ideal aggressive operator, and Drew the ideal defensive operator. They were ideal opponents.

Vanderbilt, " unconsciously to himself working more wisely than he knew . . . developed to its logical conclusion one potent element of modern civilization.

" Gravitation is the rule, and centralization the natural consequence, in society no less than in physics. Physically, morally, intellectually, in population, wealth, and intelligence, all things tend to consolidation. One singular illustration of this law is almost entirely the growth of this century. Formerly, either governments, or individuals, or, at most, small combinations of individuals, were the originators of all great works of public utility. Within the present century only has democracy found its way through the representative system into the combinations of capital, small shareholders combining to carry out the most extensive enterprises. And yet already our great corporations are fast emancipating themselves from the state, or rather subjecting the state to their own control, while individual capitalists, who long ago abandoned the attempt to compete with them, will next seek to control them. In this dangerous path of centralization Vanderbilt has taken the latest step in advance."

Drew was without constructive imagination. He could never have imagined such a scheme as Vanderbilt's. He had no initiative. But he was very astute in defending an inside position. He knew how to manipulate details with which he was familiar. Vanderbilt first attempted to capture him by manœuvre. Drew outwitted him by chicanery of unequalled subtlety, and he became enraged at this affront before all Wall Street. He now attacked the Erie railroad " with the brute force of all his millions."

Both sides employed the judiciary against the other. They sought judges complacent to their desire, and obtained injunctions from them which handicapped the other side. Armed gangs of men besieged the garrisoned offices of the rival companies. Trains manned by armed partisans were charged into each other on single railroad tracks for which the parties were contending, and the respective crews engaged in hand-to-hand combat after the collision.

Drew's colleagues among the directors of the Erie company included Jay Gould, who was his equal in chicane, and superior in financial imagination ; and Jim Fisk, a piratical blond who handled the organized violence on behalf of Erie.

This group proved too much even for Vanderbilt. He was forced to compromise with them and leave the Erie company entirely in their control.

During this contest the speculating public had grown accustomed to a new degree of wildness in the fluctuations of stock prices.

The old methods of registering price changes were unable to follow the new rates of fluctuation efficiently. There was a pressing demand for instantaneous distribution of stock prices to the rapidly increasing number of persons gambling on the large, swift changes in prices.

The unparalleled events of the Erie financial war were soon exceeded by the results of the attempts of the triumphant Erie directors to corner all the gold in the United States.

The inflation of the currency during the Civil War had

greatly increased the price of gold, as the financiers clung to gold as a measure of value, as they still do today. The fluctuations in the price of gold governed the prices of all other commodities, so gold was the central material for speculation. A special office for buying and selling gold, and registering its price, was organized during the Civil War. The president of this office devised an indicator, like a scoring board. It had two faces, one of which could be seen from inside the office, and the other from the street. The figures on the indicator were controlled by an electrical mechanism operated by the registrar of gold prices.

The prices shown on the indicators were noted by the messenger boys and carried to the various brokers' offices. The boys were often delayed, and made mistakes, so the automatic registration of prices in each broker's office, sent by the registrar from a master transmitter, was obviously desirable. Laws devised such a " Gold Reporting Telegraph," and introduced it in 1866. This primitive apparatus was evolved into a stock-ticker by Callahan.

It has been mentioned that when Edison arrived in New York in 1869, he slept in the battery room of Laws' Gold Indicator Company. On the third day after his arrival, while sitting in the transmitter room, the transmitter suddenly stopped with a crash. Within two minutes over three hundred boys besieged the office, yelling that the brokers' wires were out of order and must be fixed at once. The man in charge lost his wits in the pandemonium. Edison had learned how the apparatus worked, and after examining it, saw what was the matter ; a contact spring had broken off, and jammed two gear wheels. As he went to the man in charge to explain what was the matter, Laws rushed in, " the most excited person I had seen. He demanded of the man the cause of the trouble, but the man was speechless. I ventured to say that I knew what the trouble was, and he said, ' Fix it ! Fix it ! Be quick ! ' "

In about two hours Edison had got the whole system working again. Laws asked him who he was, and after discussing his instruments, and hearing Edison's suggestions for improvements, he appointed him general manager of the system at $300 per month. This was far more than Edison had ever received before, and an enormous salary for a twenty-one-year-old young man who had been virtually starving seventy-two hours previously.

The tremendous burst of speculation created a sharp

demand for stock-tickers. The capital of Callahan's company was increased in its first year to $1,000,000 and paid a dividend of ten per cent. Laws and Callahan presently amalgamated their companies, and Edison left Laws' employ.

The rising speculation in gold provided Edison with work and technical problems when he arrived in New York. It reached its extremest height a few months later in the autumn, when Gould and Fisk tried to complete the corner of gold. The Federal Government collected the duties on imports in gold. This helped to create a gold stringency, which the Government normally relieved by monthly sales of gold. The periodical shortages of gold became more acute in the fall or autumn, when farmers suddenly required money in exchange for crops.

In September, 1869, Gould and Fisk used the financial resources of the Erie railroad to acquire control of the relatively small amount of available gold. They obtained access to Grant, the President of the United States, by bribing his relatives. Grant was a remarkable soldier, who, after discharge from the army at the age of thirty-nine for drunkenness, rose from apparent failure, in the circumstances of the Civil War, to become commander-in-chief of the victorious army. On active service he exhibited outstanding military qualities, but in peace he showed less than the normal human capacity for the ordinary affairs of civil life.

Both his military success and his civil fecklessness appeared to be connected with his feeling of detachment from other men. He was the only American general who could conduct a battle without being perturbed by the number of casualties. Nearly all of the American generals were very political and their military judgment was warped by the consideration of the effect of casualties on public opinion, and their own political careers.

Grant had no political ambitions, interests, or understanding. He shrank from any sort of strenuous social contact with other men, and was even prudish, as he once said that no one had ever seen him naked since childhood.

He was generous, amiable, and extraordinarily casual. He supposed that clever civilians were a superior human type, and was willing to give trusting admiration to the masters of the incomprehensible activities of civil life.

Like millions of others of the simpler Americans he admired the millionaires and their apparently miraculous financial exploits. They seemed to be the finest demonstra-

tion of the exercise of the American ideals of personal freedom, and the accumulation of private property.

Grant felt honoured by invitations to the parties of Fisk.
He was delighted to listen to any suggestions from such a
great financier on how the Government finances might be
conducted more efficiently.

Fisk and his friends convinced him that the sale of gold by
the Government was bad for trade and agriculture, and persuaded him to suspend it. After Grant had given the order,
he left for, or was got away to, an inaccessible part of the
country.

Gould and Fisk now increased the artificial shortage of
gold by buying all that came into the market. Gold prices
soon rose to extreme heights, as foreign trade could not be
conducted without it. At the same time an attack on Vanderbilt's stocks was started. The price of gold on Tuesday,
September 21st, rose to 138. On Wednesday the price of the
stock of Vanderbilt's Central Railroad fell from 198 to 177.

" While Vanderbilt was hurrying back by special train
from Albany, Director James Fisk, Jr., was manipulating
gold in the manner peculiar to himself, offering great bets
as to the point it would reach, proclaiming his intention and
ability to break Vanderbilt down, and boasting of the power
of his combination, in which he even dared openly to include
the President of the United States himself."

All legitimate business was paralysed, and " crowds of
desperate men only left Broad Street to haunt the corridors of
taverns, and to buy and sell and gamble, till the night was
wellnigh worn away."

On Thursday the price of gold was driven still higher, in
spite of opposition from the Government, which was now
becoming thoroughly alarmed.

On Friday morning the streets, buildings, and windows
were filled with spectators who had come with fascination
to watch their own ruin. The Fisk party knew that the
Government was no longer passive, and that they could
continue to force the price only by pure bluff. Fisk's brokers
made quick successive offers without a taker, and ran the
bidding up to 162. Suddenly a Government broker began
to accept the bids, and the price collapsed to 134. " Mean-
while, across the street, Fisk was vapouring in his wild way,
refusing offers of gold at 135, because he was buying at 160,
proclaiming himself the ' Napoleon of Wall Street.' "

The Government sellers now demanded from Fisk the

settlement of their margins. He agreed, and then disappeared through a back door.

During the day, " men forgot to act, and openly displayed their inmost natures . . . they seemed dazed or drunken ; no one knew where he stood, or how he stood ; but the mob of brokers and of lookers on surged to and fro, and in and out, some howling, yelling and gesticulating, others silent and confounded, and others again, almost crazy. Some, indeed, were quite crazy. . . ."

While Fisk had been brazening out the field, his colleague Gould had secretly withdrawn his money. By Friday evening, the clearing house found itself overwhelmed with an inextricable confusion of transactions totalling $500,000,000. The attempt to unravel the confusion was abandoned, and speculators cut their losses. Fisk was temporarily bankrupt, but Gould had deserted him, and escaped. They had engineered the attempted corner, and disorganized the commerce of America, on a liquid capital as small as $2,000,000.

As mechanical superintendent of the Gold Indicator System, Edison had to supervise the central transmitter of gold prices. It was difficult to make the machine work fast enough to keep up with the wild fluctuations in prices, but it was speeded up by putting a paper-weight on it. On the morning of " Black " Friday the apparatus fell behind, but Edison had made it catch up with the current price by one o'clock.

He " sat on the top of the Western Union Telegraph booth (in the gold exchange office) to watch the surging, crazy crowd. One man came to the booth, grabbed a pencil, and attempted to write a message to Boston. The first stroke went clear off the blank ; he was so excited that he had the operator write the message for him. Amid great excitement Speyer, the banker, went crazy and it took five men to hold him ; and everybody lost his head. The Western Union operator came to me and said : ' Shake, Edison, we are O.K. We haven't got a cent.' I felt very happy because we were poor. These occasions are very enjoyable to a poor man, but they occur rarely."

Edison overheard messages which indicated there was some sort of conspiracy between the Government and Wall Street. He observed Fisk in " a velvet corduroy coat and a very peculiar vest. He was very chipper, and seemed to be light-hearted and happy. Sitting around the room were about a dozen fine-looking men. All had the complexion of cadavers.

There was a basket of champagne."

Edison had witnessed through his presence in Wall Street on September 24th, 1868, and his connection with the gold price indicator, the power of telegraphic instruments in contemporary commerce. He had seen men go crazy after reading the indicator's figures. Six days after " Black " Friday he started a business with F. L. Pope, a talented operator friend, to design and operate public and private telegraphic and other electrical equipment. Early in 1869 the *Telegrapher* published the news that " T. A. Edison has resigned the situation in the Western Union office, Boston, and will devote his time to bringing out his inventions." This was the first occasion in history on which a man aged twenty-two truly announced that he would make invention his profession.

In the announcement of the new firm in the *Telegrapher*, Pope, Edison & Co. described themselves as " electrical engineers." It is said that this was the first occasion when the term was used in the professional sense. It was an important contribution towards the conception of a new profession, the consulting electrical engineer.

Pope and Edison invented a stock-ticker which could be worked on one wire, and devised a system for importers and exchange brokers that was cheaper than the existing gold indicator service. This and other inventions interested the Gold and Stock Telegraph Company, which presently absorbed the Pope and Edison firm.

The president of this company, Marshall Lefferts, asked Edison to undertake the general improvement of the ticker apparatus. Edison rapidly secured a number of patents for improvements. In particular, he devised the " unison stop," by which all tickers could be brought back to a zero position by the operator in the central transmitting office. This saved the expense of sending mechanics to offices to synchronize tickers which had got out of step. Lefferts decided to buy the rights in Edison's early ticker inventions. When Edison received the request to go to his office, he had fixed in his mind a price of $5,000, and in any case, not less than $3,000. Lefferts asked him how much he wanted, but he suddenly lost his nerve, and dared not ask for $5,000, so he asked Lefferts to make an offer. Lefferts said : " How would $40,000 strike you ? " Edison nearly fainted, but managed to accept. At that time, he still measured the value of an invention by the time and trouble he had given to it, " and not by what the invention was worth to others."

Lefferts then handed a cheque for $40,000 to Edison, who had never received money in the form of a cheque before. When he presented the cheque it was handed back to him because it was not endorsed. Owing to his deafness he could not understand the clerk's explanation. He suspected that he had been swindled, and hurried back to Lefferts, who laughed at him, endorsed the cheque, and sent a young man with him back to the bank, to testify to his identity. The bank clerk then paid out the money in large packets of small bills, as a joke. Edison took the pile of bills home and stayed up with them all night, in fear of having them stolen. On the next morning he asked the amused Lefferts what he should do with them, and was advised to start a bank account.

Edison was now able, in 1870, at the age of twenty-three, to begin manufacturing electrical apparatus on a considerable scale. He employed fifty men in making large numbers of stock-tickers for Lefferts. He started double shifts as business increased, and worked on both of them as his own foreman. He did not sleep more than a few half-hours during each twenty-four hours. He drank strong coffee and smoked strong cigars without restraint. He drove his men on piece-work. They could earn high wages, and were treated with a rough cheerfulness as long as they fitted in with his methods, but they were discharged without consideration if they did not.

The staff of Edison's first shop included S. Bergmann and J. S. Schuckert, the founders of two immense German electrical engineering firms bearing their names, and J. Kruesi, who became the chief engineer of the General Electric Works at Schenectady. In later years Edison engaged A. E. Kennelly, the eminent discoverer of the Kennelly-Heaviside layer, and E. G. Acheson, the inventor of carborundum. He had an aptitude for recognizing talented men.

Within a few years Edison acquired forty-six patents for improvements of stock-tickers. The American patent law permits the protection of many details not patentable under European law, but even after allowing for this difference, and that none of his stock-ticker patents was of the first degree of importance, and that he had already begun to exploit the assistance of talented colleagues, Edison's fertility was remarkable. His power of managing others was not less remarkable. Dyer and Martin have observed that he used men up in the achievement of his aims as ruthlessly as Napoleon or Grant.

At the age of twenty-three, in a works financed out of his own inventions, he had attracted and led such men as Bergmann and Schuckert. His choice of stock-tickers as a subject of inventive work showed he could recognize major social phenomena when they rose around him. He worked at tickers because they had obvious commercial and therefore social importance. He was without personal interest in speculation, and never speculated in his life, but he was willing to provide improved machines to make speculation easier. It was easy even for minor inventors to see that tickers were important in the New York of 1869.

By this time Edison must have become aware of the greatness of his inventive talent. He showed rare realistic talent in not spurning a field occupied by many other lesser talents, and in not succumbing to the vanity of risking his great talent on entirely new ideas beyond the range of the others. As he did not speculate in stocks, so he did not speculate in invention. He missed several first-class scoops through his refusal to gamble in invention, but by his example he helped to remove the practice of invention from the sphere of gambling and magic. He helped to socialize invention, demonstrate its part in the development of human society, and establish it as a new profession.

He worked with extreme energy on many aspects of telegraphy in his first independent years. The development of automatic telegraphy required apparatus which would work at much higher speeds than hand-operated apparatus. It was found that the hand apparatus, which worked satisfactorily at the usual speeds, would not work properly at high speeds, owing to the effects of electrical inertia, or self-induction. The signals were drawn out, and lost definition.

Edison invented a method of preventing this. He exhibited it at the Centennial Exposition in 1876, and it was adjudicated a reward by Kelvin, who was then Sir William Thomson.

Kelvin reported that "the electro-magnetic shunt with soft iron core, invented by Mr. Edison, utilizing Professor Henry's discovery of electro-magnetic induction in a single circuit to produce a momentary reversal of the live current at the instant when the battery is thrown off and so cut off the chemical marks sharply at the proper instant, is the electrical secret of the great speed he has achieved. . . . It deserves award as a very important step in land telegraphy."

Edison was sent to demonstrate the automatic system in

England in 1873. He claimed his demonstrations were successful, but he was unable to persuade the British authorities to adopt his system. While in London he was asked if he would care to test his apparatus using a coiled cable 2,200 miles long as the telegraph wire.

Edison did not fully understand the theory of electrical self-induction, and did not foresee that the self-induction of the coiled cable would have an enormous value. He was astounded when a Morse dot normally one thirty-secondth of an inch long was extended into a line about thirty feet long. His ignorance of scientific theory raised criticism and opposition, especially among highly trained scientists and engineers without inventive talent. His insight into science was derived from intense practical experience of apparatuses involving scientific principles. When Kelvin invented an apparatus he embodied a scientific principle. Some of his electrometers look like a materialization of textbook diagrams on the theory of electrostatics. Edison's mental process worked in the reverse manner. His scientific ideas were abstractions drawn from apparatuses with which he had profound familiarity. His opinions on any subject of which he had experimental knowledge were always worth consideration, though his explanations were usually inaccurate and often wrong.

Edison introduced practical quadruplex telegraphy in 1874. This was his first major inventive achievement. It enables four messages, two in each direction, to be sent simultaneously over the same wire. The duplex, in which two messages are sent in opposite directions simultaneously on the same wire, had already been invented by Stearns. Edison devised a diplex system, in which two messages could be sent simultaneously in the same direction on one wire. He obtained the quadruplex by combining the duplex and diplex.

The functioning of the apparatus depends on two signalling currents. One current is made to transmit by altering its direction, and the other by varying its strength. The alterations in direction and in strength may be received independently by suitable relays at the other end of the wire. In this way, two messages may be sent simultaneously. Four messages may be sent by duplexing each of the signalling currents. This is done by arranging that the outgoing signal current shall operate the receiver at the distant station but not the receiver at the home station.

Suppose a dummy wire, whose electrical resistance and

capacity are exactly equal to those of the main wire, is connected to the end of the main wire in the home station. If the signalling current is sent into the connected wires, one half will go through the main wire, and the other half through the dummy. Suppose, now, that the main wire and the dummy wire have each been wound an equal number of times, but in opposite directions, round the iron core of the home relay magnet. Then the signalling current from the home station will not operate the home receiver, because the two currents will cancel each other's magnetizing effect on the home receiver. But the current will not be split at the distant station, so it will operate the distant receiver.

Edison said the invention of the quadruplex system " required a peculiar effort of the mind, such as the imagining of eight different things moving simultaneously on a mental plane, without anything to demonstrate their efficiency."

It seems that he visualized the eight instruments simultaneously, and tried to foresee how they would react together. He did not try to analyse the properties of the instruments and circuits theoretically.

His concentration on these mental efforts affected the normal operation of his memory. On one occasion he had to attend the City Hall to pay taxes before a certain hour in order to avoid a surcharge. An official suddenly asked him his name. He could not remember it, and lost his place in the queue, which made him too late to avoid the surcharge.

He did not show more than the minimum necessary interest in money. As long as he had sufficient for his needs he was satisfied. He never applied his mind earnestly to money-making.

He combined lack of special interest in money with an original insistence on commercial practicality in invention. This shows that he was a social theorist. He believed a good invention must conform with the criterion of commercial success, yet he did not care whether or not he made money out of inventions. It is frequently supposed that Edison's insistence on the criterion of commercial success showed that he was mercenary, and wished to make invention a tool of acquisition. His behaviour shows that he disinterestedly put invention at the service of what he conceived to be the proper social machinery, capitalist commerce. His view was far in advance of the old conception that the justification of invention is the enhancement of the dignity of human nature through exhibitions of cleverness, and that the practical application of invention is a vulgar activity of secondary importance.

He recognized that invention must have social justification. He assumed that the nineteenth-century American capitalists' criterion of justification was correct, and therefore judged invention by that criterion.

As he made relatively little money for himself out of his inventions he evidently did not apply the same criterion for judging his own private, personal success. His behaviour shows that his public and private views of invention were not the same. He was casual with his private wealth.

He did not employ book-keepers until the chaos of his finances prevented him from getting on with his work. He lost most of the royalties he should have received from his early patents through employing an unsatisfactory patent lawyer. A man of his ability would not have lost so much if he had been primarily interested in acquiring money.

The famous German theoretical and experimental chemist, Professor Nernst, invented an electric lamp, with a filament made of rare earths which conduct electricity and emit a bright light at high temperatures. The filament had to be heated by a surrounding platinum coil before it lighted up, so about fifteen seconds passed before it reached full brilliancy. The details of the lamp were complicated, and with the delay in reaching maximum illumination, prevented it from having more than a transitory commercial success. It gave way before the superior qualities of the carbon filament lamp, which was developed mainly by Edison.

When Edison met Nernst, he talked on his favourite topic of the need for inventors to be businesslike and to invent what commerce required. He said that academic scientists generally failed to appreciate the commercial problems of invention, and did not offer inventions to industry in a practicable form.

Nernst listened to the strictures on the unpractical and unbusinesslike qualities of professors. He quietly asked Edison how much he had made out of the carbon filament lamp. Edison replied that he had made nothing out of it. Nernst then asked Edison if he knew what price he had secured for the rights in the rare earths lamp. Edison said he did not know. Nernst replied that the A.E.G. had paid $250,000 for them.

This story is usually related as a proof that academic scientists are not so impractical as hard-headed practical

c

scientists, such as Edison, imagine.

It may also be interpreted as showing that Nernst's commercial sense was keener than Edison's, and that he was willing to receive a large sum of money for an invention whose commercial success was uncertain, and subsequently proved moderate.

Edison did not say that inventors should try to get more than an invention was worth. He said that they should make inventions which would be a commercial success. This did not even imply that the inventors should receive any money at all for them.

The attitude to invention of the graduate of the telegraphs of the Woolly West and of Wall Street was ethically superior to the attitude of the eminent graduate of German scholarship.

Edison's behaviour shows that desire for private profit was not the spur to his inventiveness. His demand that inventions should be commercially successful did not imply that he should make a large private fortune out of them.

It is possible for an invention to be commercially successful without one man making more profit out of it than any other man. In fact, it may be commercially successful if every member of the community makes an equal profit out of it. It is often said that inventions would never be made if no one had any prospect of making large private profits out of them. Edison's conduct is in contradiction with this view, and his emphasis on the importance of the commercial success of inventions does not necessarily imply that there will be no invention unless inventors, or some other individuals, make large profits out of inventions.

Quadruplex telegraphy was very successful in the United States. It greatly increased the volume of business that could be transmitted over existing wires, and reduced the capital expenditure on new lines. The effects of the very variable windfall and drought on the resistance of the earth, and the insulation of the line, increased the difficulties of working the system in England.

Edison's quadruplex and other telegraphic inventions were used as pawns in financial operations by Jay Gould. The companies that owned his inventions were offered about $1,000,000 for them. Gould used the existence of this offer to depress the value, and secure the control, of the Western Union stock. He then repudiated the offer. The legal struggles over the repudiation lasted thirty years. The reactionaries who controlled the telegraph companies opposed the extension of automatic telegraphy, and the development, which became extensive before 1880, was allowed to die.

Edison had personal dealings with Gould in the early stages of this affair. He took part in secret consultations with him, in which the negotiators entered Gould's house through the servants' entrance at night, to evade the observations of spies from rival companies. Gould paid him $30,000 for his personal interest in the quadruplex, but evaded paying him anything for about three years' other work.

Dyer and Martin quote Edison as expressing contrary opinions on the treatment he received from Gould. On one occasion he said : " I never had any grudge against him, because he was so able in his line, and as long as my part was successful, the money with me was a secondary consideration." But in 1876 Edison had written bitter complaints that his relations with Gould had been " a long, unbroken disappointment," and that he " had to live."

Edison said that Gould had no sense of humour. He had a peculiar expression which seemed to indicate insanity. He was extremely mean. He was very angry when the rent of his stock-ticker was raised a few dollars. He had the machine removed, and preferred to do without it, in spite of the great inconvenience, rather than pay. He worked very hard and collected and thoroughly studied the statistics bearing on his financial affairs. The extent of his relations with persons in official life was surprising. He was entirely non-constructive, and was interested in money only. " His conscience seemed to be atrophied, but that may be due to the fact that he was contending with men who never had any." Gould did not care whether his companies were a success or a failure. When he secured control of the Western Union, Edison " knew no further progress in telegraphy was possible, and I went into other lines " of invention. Gould's colleague in the crippling of telegraphy in America was General Eckert, who had been Assistant Secretary of War to Stanton during the Civil War. The close connection between the victors of the war and the characteristic technological and financial post-war developments is significant. It provides one of the reasons why Americans were supine under the activities of such men as Vanderbilt and Gould. They did not fundamentally disapprove of them. Like Edison, they were prepared to admire their ability even when robbed by them of payment for years of work. Edison was not interested in money, but he could admire Gould who was interested in nothing else. This admiration of principles which one does not practise is a feature of the psychology of religion. The frenzies of the gold corner were manifestations of herd religious emotions. Men did not go crazy because they were ruined, as ruin was only a temporary condition for an American in 1869. He could not remain destitute long in such a rapidly developing country. The frenzies were due to excessive perturbations in the current religious worship of wealth. Everyone believed that owning wealth was of vital importance, and that loss of wealth meant damnation. The hysteria was induced by the fear of damnation by the god of wealth.

Within a few years of establishing his first shop Edison worked simultaneously on nearly fifty inventions. He assisted Scholes in the development of his invention of the typewriter, he invented the mimeograph, or stencil from which numerous copies of written matter may be pulled. The stencil was cut by a stylus, used as a pen, whose point was driven in and out rapidly by an electric or pneumatic motor, so that it left a line of five holes along the strokes of the writing.

He also invented paraffin paper, now used for wrapping sweets and candy, and many other purposes.

The growth of the telegraph stimulated many attempts to invent multiplex systems, by which one wire could be used to transmit simultaneously a large number of messages. Several inventors were trying to devise multiplex systems in which the various simultaneous signal currents were picked out by tuning-forks.

The transmission of sounds was incidental in these telegraphs to the transmission of ordinary dot-and-dash messages. The inventive workers on this sort of apparatus included A. Graham Bell, Edison, and Asa Gray. It was natural that one or two of them would begin to alter the perspective in which they were working, and consider the apparatuses as transmitters of sounds by electricity, instead of transmitters of multiple signals by electricity with the assistance of sounds. The conception of an electrical apparatus for transmitting human speech followed as an extension of this direction of thought.

Inventors had attacked the problem of the electrical transmission of human speech directly at an earlier date. The first electrical machine which could speak was devised by the German Professor Reis about 1860. He named it the " telephone." It depended on the starting and stopping of an electric current by a diaphragm made to vibrate by the sound waves of the human voice. Reis and the inventors who followed him could not make the machine repeat more than a few syllables before the make-and-break contact was thrown out of adjustment, so it was not a practical invention. A Reis instrument was explained to Bell by Joseph Henry, and Edison also had an account of it. No doubt Gray also knew it. Bell was the first to see how a practical telephone could be made. He was the son of A. M. Bell, a lecturer on elocution at University College, London, and an original worker on the analysis of speech. Graham Bell had grown up amidst studies of phonetics, vocal physiology, and original thought on the mechanism of speech.

This background of knowledge probably increased his confidence in attempting to invent a practical telephone. Workers less familiar with the mechanism of the human voice may have given too much weight to the belief that sounds as complicated as human speech could not be transmitted without an equally complicated machine. Bell discovered that speech could be continuously transmitted by an exquisitely simple mechanism. He found that if an iron diaphragm was made to vibrate near a permanent magnet with a coil of wire wound round it, a current was induced in the coil. Suppose somebody speaks at the diaphragm. It will vibrate in unison with the sound waves started by the voice. The voice will be transformed into a varying current. If this current is sent through a wire to the coil on the permanent magnet of a similar instrument, it will attract its diaphragm back and forth, and reproduce the vibrations in the diaphragm of the first instrument. In reproducing the same sequence of vibrations it will reproduce the same sequence of sounds.

Bell's patent was registered on March 7th, 1876. A few hours later, on the same day, Gray made a claim for a similar patent. Edison had constructed in 1875 a resonator for analysing telegraph currents, which could reproduce human speech, but which had not been put to that use.

Bell's original telephone was a magnificent invention, but it had serious limitations. The transmitting current was produced by the unaided energy of the human voice, which had made the iron disc vibrate in a magnetic field and so produce the current. The energy of the sound waves from the human voice is very small, so the energy of the transmitting current was very small. The current was too faint to be effective beyond a short distance.

Edison now made two inventions which removed this limitation, and created the practical telephone which could communicate over long distances. He showed how to put virtually unlimited energy into the transmission. He placed a button of carbon or lamp-black against the disc. When the disc was made to vibrate by the waves from the voice, the pressure of the disc on the carbon varied. He found that the electrical resistance of the carbon varied with the variations in pressure. Thus the carbon button could be arranged to act as variable resistance in a circuit containing a current of any required strength. He placed the button in the primary circuit of an induction coil connected with a voltaic battery, and the distant receiver, of the Bell type, was put into the circuit of the secondary coil. This arrangement enabled the voice to be transmitted by high voltage currents, which could overcome the resistance of long wires, and hence long distances.

At this time Edison was again working in connection with the Western Union. Their telephone department was managed by Twombly, Vanderbilt's son-in-law. The controllers of the Western Union started the customary financial warfare with the controllers of the company exploiting Bell's patent. The Western Union pirated Bell's receiver, and Bell's company pirated Edison's transmitter.

Edison now sought some payment for his carbon transmitter. He had privately decided that $25,000 would be a fair price, and then asked for an offer. He was promptly offered $100,000. He said he would accept it on the condition that it was paid to him at the rate of $6,000 yearly for seventeen years, the life of the patent. He was glad to make this arrangement because he could not trust himself not to spend any available money on experiments, " as his ambition was about four times too large for his business capacity." It will be noticed that he might have invested the money, and have received $6,000 interest for seventeen years, and still have possessed the capital at the end of the period. He said that the arrangement protected him from worry for seventeen years.

At about this time Jay Gould renewed his stock exchange campaigns against the Western Union. He had bought Page's patent, which was believed to cover all forms of electro-magnetic relay. The Western Union asked Edison if he could invent a method of moving a lever at the end of a wire, which did not involve a magnet. He immediately.

solved this problem by an application of a device he had patented in 1875..

He had discovered that moistened chalk became slippery when a current was passed through it. Thus a lever held at rest by friction against the moistened chalk would be released when current was sent through the chalk. This invention was sufficient to check Gould's use of the Page patent against the Western Union.

Edison was again offered $100,000 for the rights, and again stipulated the payment of $6,000 for seventeen years. Thus he received $12,000 yearly for seventeen years for these two inventions.

The same invention was employed again in a patent contest in England. The Bell and Edison interests had started independent companies in England to exploit their patents. The Edison company found that they would not be able to pirate the Bell receiver under the British patent law, so they cabled Edison for instructions. He replied that he could soon relieve them from dependence on the Bell receiver. He invented a new receiver depending on the slippery chalk phenomenon. He mounted a cylinder of chalk on an axle which could be rotated steadily. One end of a small metal rod rested on the surface of the chalk, and the other end was attached to a mica diaphragm. The surface of the chalk cylinder was moistened with a solution of various salts. When the cylinder was rotated, it tended to drag the end of the rod, owing to the friction between the chalk surface and the rod. The drag on the rod, in turn, distorted the diaphragm at the other end. The receiving current from the telephone wire was now sent through the contact between the moistened chalk surface and the metal rod. It varied the degree of friction in proportion to its strength, owing to electrolysis on the chalk surface, and made the rod slip in step with the current variations. The slithering of one end of the rod made the mica diaphragm vibrate in unison. In this way, the mica diaphragm reproduced the sounds spoken into the distant transmitter. This new Edison receiver was a loud-speaker. The energy which worked it came from the rotation of the wheel, and could be far greater than the energy of the transmitting current. This receiver assured the freedom of Edison's English company from interference by the Bell company. The two companies then amalgamated to resist the pretensions of the British Post Office. Edison received £30,000, or $150,000, from the amalgamated company for his patent rights.

Edison's production of two first-class inventions, the non-magnetic relay and the loud-speaking telephone receiver, in order to destroy the monopolies of other patents, is unparalleled. On nearly all other occasions in history, powerful inventions have not been produced to order at short notice. They have usually been produced after years of difficult struggle. Edison produced both of these inventions as weapons in stock-exchange fights. The achievement exhibited invention in a new aspect. Hitherto it had been regarded as an uncontrollable activity, like the composition of poetry. Edison now showed that first-class invention could be done to order. This was an important contribution to sociology, as it helped to destroy the belief that invention depended on unpredictable inspiration. It strengthened the hope that humanity would learn how to reduce invention from a fortuitous into a controlled process of development of the machinery of civilization.

Edison's London staff, which had to demonstrate his telephones, included twenty carefully selected young American mechanics, G. Bernard Shaw, Samuel Insull, and other men who became well known.

Shaw's experiences with Edison's London company had a formative influence on his ideas. He was about twenty-four years old, and was beginning to formulate his criticism of society in sociological novels. The first, written in 1879, was never published, and the second, *The Irrational Knot*, was written in 1880, after working for the Edison company. Shaw had to assist in the demonstrations of the loud-speaking telephone to prospective clients. He has given some interesting reminiscences of the American electricians in the preface which he wrote for the novel in 1905. They knew so little about the theory of electricity that he was able to hold his own with them, as he had read something, and even knew a relative of Bell. They were extremely energetic and profane, despised English class distinctions, were proud of American ideals of liberty, and cheerfully bore relentless bullying from American foremen. They attacked difficulties with courage and energy, but a large part of the energy was wasted through ignorance. They were rescued from false starts by English colleagues who often had better scientific qualifications but less initiative.

Shaw's second novel, and first published work, exhibits an intense interest in class psychology. He wished to contrast the characteristics of members of the English leisure class with those of members of the skilled artisan or operator class, by depicting the intrusion of a talented artisan into the leisure class. The intruding hero is named Edward Conolly, an American mechanic and electrician, of Irish and Italian descent. He becomes assistant mechanic to Lord Carbury, an English nobleman with scientific hobbies. He invents an electric motor of great commercial promise. Carbury and his rich relatives, including one named Lind, finance a company for the exploitation of the invention. Conolly now has reputation and prospects of wealth. He is acquainted with Lind's daughter, a girl with natural charm, but without training, in virtue of her membership of the leisure class. Their marriage proves unhappy, as Conolly cannot adapt himself to the leisure class incompetence of his wife. She then elopes with a rich Etonian with an impressive figure and manners and an Oxford literary education, in the belief that he has more feeling and sensitiveness than Conolly. She swiftly finds he is conceited and without creative ability. Presently she meets Conolly again. It has become clear that she will not be able to abandon the habits of the leisure class, so their reunion is impracticable. Conolly perceives that he has married beneath him in terms of ability.

The personality of the imaginary character Edward Conolly was very different from the personality of Edison, but probably it would never have been created if Edison had never existed. Conolly was represented as a very educable man. Edison was not educable, and remained uncultivated. Shaw could not have idealized his American colleagues in London, because they were extremely undisciplined, while Conolly had exceptional self-control. Shaw adopted from Edison and his American mechanics the elements of creative ability and independence of British upper-class manners. He needed a character independent of the ideas and habits of the different English social classes in order to criticize those ideas and habits. In 1880 the type of an American electrical inventor seemed to him to be particularly suitable for that purpose. His choice was an indication of the sociological interest of that type.

4

Edison's first wife was named Mary Stillwell, whom he married in 1871. He had met her, while she was still a schoolgirl, on the doorstep of his laboratory. She and her sister happened to stand there for shelter during a shower of rain. Edison immediately liked her, and presently asked her to marry him. Her parents said she was too young to be married immediately. During the delay deemed necessary by her parents, Edison provided occupation for her in his laboratory. She assisted in his experiments on the invention of paraffin paper.

Their first child, a daughter, was born in 1873. At that time Edison was still working in his Newark workshop. He became dissatisfied with this in 1876. His wife was expecting a second child at this time, which proved to be his first son. Edison invited his father to search for a suitable site for a new laboratory and home, and offered him the post of house-manager or caretaker. Edison senior recommended a quiet place named Menlo Park, about twenty-five miles from New York. The place was not too accessible for casual visitors, and allowed him to have his home and work close together.

A second son was born after he had been at Menlo Park two years. He no doubt hoped that the country air would protect the health of his family, but unfortunately Mrs. Edison was delicate, and presently was infected with typhoid fever, of which she died in 1884. Edison left Menlo Park soon afterwards.

His inventive fertility between 1876 and 1884, or the ages of twenty-nine and thirty-seven years, cannot be paralleled in history. It will be noticed that he had two children during the same period. His sexual power does not appear to have been seriously impaired by his extraordinary mental and physical exertions. During much of the period he worked on an average nearly twenty hours a day.

5

Edison designed the laboratory at Menlo Park according to his own wishes. Architecturally, it resembled a small Methodists' chapel. It was a plain rectangular building with two floors. He had not previously had the opportunity of working in a laboratory of his own design ; he had had to work in such rooms as he could rent, or was provided with, by companies who financed some particular research.

Edison's Menlo Park laboratory was a new type of insti-tution. It was the first institution designed for professional inventing. Hitherto, inventors had been amateurs who had means to work out their ideas, or had means provided for them by some company which employed them on its own premises. The inventor had an idea. He took this idea to a capitalist. The capitalist helped him to put this one idea into a practical form. He might supply him with money and workshops for this purpose. Edison's aim at Menlo Park was fundamentally different. His laboratory was not designed for the perfection of one invention, but of all inventions. He intended it to be a place where persons who needed inventions of any sort could have their needs satisfied. He aimed at inventing anything. Edison wished to change from invention by inspiration to invention by request. He wished to escape from the usual concentration on one line accidentally chosen, to work on all required lines. He wished to generalize and professionalize invention.

His first major work at Menlo Park was concerned with the carbon telephone transmitter. He was attempting to invent a transmitter better than Bell's, at the request of companies to which he was attached. He remembered that when he was working on multiple telegraphs, some years before, he had devised various forms of resistance to represent the dummy line, whose part in duplex and quadruplex telegraphy has already been explained. He had found that resistance could be conveniently made out of loose carbon pressed together. The size of the resistance could be varied by varying the pressure. He invented the carbon telephone transmitter by arranging for the pressure on carbon to be varied by the impulse of sound waves from the human voice.

In an earlier research he had assisted Scholes in the development of the typewriter. He undertook this work in the interest of the telegraph companies, as it was thought that typewriters might be of use to telegraph operators. The replacement of general handwriting by machinery was not the primary aim of Edison's work on typewriters, but the assistance of telegraphy.

Edison's powers and limitations were illustrated by his experiments on what he named " etheric force " in 1875. He believed he had discovered that when a telegraphic battery circuit was broken, it might under certain conditions produce sparks in unconnected circuits. It appeared that some " etheric force " was capable of producing electrical effects at a distance. The nature of the circuits used seemed to show that the effects were not due to ordinary electromagnetic induction. Edison wrote detailed accounts of numerous experiments on this supposed new force.

It has naturally been assumed that Edison had discovered some effects due to radio waves. But a careful study of the descriptions of his experimental arrangements seems to show that the energy used in his circuits would have been insufficient to produce electro-magnetic waves capable of making sparks observable with his equipment. The sparks were probably due to some spurious effect. Edison saw that if his results were genuine, they implied the possibility of electrical communication without wires.

He explained that " the cumbersome appliances of transmitting ordinary electricity, such as telegraph poles, insulating knobs, cable sheathings and so on, may be left out of the problem of quick and cheap telegraphic transmission ; and a great saving of time and labor accomplished."

He did not persevere with his experiments, so any chance that he might have invented communication by radio waves vanished.

Edison applied for a patent in 1885 for wireless communication by electrostatic induction. He erected two high masts separated by a distance. A metal surface was fixed at the top of each mast. The metal surface on the top of the sending mast was connected with one of his loud-speaking telephones near its base. Transmission was accomplished by discharging the induction coil through the aerial into the metal surface at the top of the mast. The electrostatic charge on the metal at the top of the sending mast induced a charge on the metal at the top of the distant receiving mast, which sent a current down the aerial, and produced a click in the telephone. When radio-telegraphy was invented, it could not be developed without Edison's system of aerials, though it employed electro-magnetic waves instead of electrostatic induction for the transmission of energy across space. Rivals of the Marconi Company wished to secure his aerial patent in order to obtain a share of control over the development of the Marconi system. Edison refused their offers and sold his rights to the Marconi Company in 1903.

Edison invented the phonograph or gramophone at Menlo Park in 1877. It was his most original invention. When his application for a patent was submitted to the Patents Office, no previous reference could be found in its records to any suggestion for a machine for permanently recording the human voice in a form which enabled it to be reproduced. Bell's telephone invention had drawn attention to the problems of the reproduction of speech. Edison had joined in the extensive efforts to improve the telephone, and had introduced his carbon transmitter. He had become familiar with the elastic properties of discs, which enabled them to vibrate in tune with the vibrations of the voice. Though the familiarity with this property was essential to his discovery, he did not approach voice recording from this aspect. Some time before, he had invented an automatic recording telegraph. This consisted of a disc of paper, which could be rotated round a vertical axis, as in an ordinary gramophone. The paper disc was set in rotation, and the dots and dashes of the incoming message were embossed on it along a volute spiral. Thus several of the features of the record of the telegraphic message were similar to those of the present gramophone record. When the disc telegraphic record was removed from the receiving machine and put into a similar transmitting machine and rotated, the embossed marks lifted a contact lever up and down, and thus sent the message on to the next station. The apparatus could transmit Morse messages at the rate of several hundred words per minute. It was noticed that if the disc record was rotated very quickly, the rattling of the lever was raised to a musical note. Edison now reasoned that if the disc could produce a musical note it might be made to produce sounds like human speech. He knew from telephone experience that diaphragms would vibrate in tune with the vibrations of a human voice, and that these vibrations were of a considerable size and could be made to do mechanical work. He had devised a toy to illustrate this. He concluded that if he could record the movements of the diaphragm on some sort of disc or strip, and then use the marks on the record to set another diaphragm in motion, the second diaphragm would reproduce the sounds which had fallen on the first diaphragm.

He designed a grooved cylinder which could be rotated around a horizontal axis. The cylinder was to be covered with tin-foil. A diaphragm with a needle was fixed over the foil-covered cylinder so that when words were spoken near it, the vibrations started in the diaphragm were embossed by the needle on the soft tin-foil. A sketch of the machine was prepared, and marked $18. Edison's mechanics worked on a minimum wage and piece-work system. If the job cost more than the estimate, the mechanic received the minimum wage; if it cost less, he received in addition to his wage the difference saved. The phonograph sketch was given to John Kruesi. When the machine was nearly finished Kruesi asked what it was for. Edison told him it was to record talking. Kruesi thought the idea absurd. When the machine was finished, Edison shouted at the diaphragm : " Mary had a little lamb," etc. He then adjusted the reproducing diaphragm and rotated the cylinder. " The machine reproduced it perfectly. I was never so taken aback in my life. Everybody was astonished. I was always afraid of things that worked the first time. Long experience proved that there were great drawbacks found generally before they could be got commercial ; but here was something there was no doubt of."

Edison's power of imagining the scope of invention is illustrated by his summary of the possibilities of the phonograph in 1878. He wrote :

" Among the many uses to which the phonograph will be applied are the following :

" 1. Letter writing and all kinds of dictation without the aid of a stenographer.

" 2. Phonographic books, which will speak to blind people without effort on their part.

" 3. The teaching of elocution.

" 4. Reproduction of music.

" 5. The ' Family Record '—a registry of sayings, reminiscences, etc., by members of a family in their own voices, and of the last words of dying persons.

" 6. Music-boxes and toys.

" 7. Clocks that should announce in articulate speech the time for going home, going to meals, etc.

" 8. The preservation of languages by exact reproduction of the manner of pronouncing.

" 9. Educational purposes ; such as preserving the explanations made by a teacher, so that the pupil can refer to them at any moment, and spelling or other lessons placed upon the phonograph for convenience in committing to memory.

" 10. Connection with the telephone, so as to make that instrument an auxiliary in the transmission of permanent and invaluable records, instead of being the recipient of momentary and fleeting communication."

The early development of the phonograph was indifferently successful. As the machine was too crude to satisfy artistic feeling, it could not immediately succeed as a musical instrument. It was exploited as an astonishing toy. Its possibilities as a mechanical stenographer were the first to receive serious commercial attention, but the attempts failed, as ordinary clerical staffs found the operation of the machine too difficult. Edison neglected the phonograph for the next ten years. In 1888, after he had launched his incandescent electric light system, he returned to the phonograph, and rapidly improved it by intensive work. On one occasion he worked continuously on the machine for five consecutive days and nights.

Edison's performances with sound-reproducing machines such as the telephone and the phonograph are exceptionally remarkable because of his deafness. He had to depend in a large degree on the hearing of his assistants in the researches on the improvement in the quality of the mechanical articulation. His sister-in-law has written that he often suffered from severe earache at Menlo Park. His deafness may be contrasted with the previous acoustical interests and trained hearing of Bell, and of the musician D. E. Hughes, who invented the microphone and the printing telegraph. Edison's work on the invention of acoustical apparatus did not receive any impulse from long-cultivated special interests such as elocution or music. His deafness may have given him an unconscious interest in acoustical appliances, and he may have had some hope that he could invent a mechanical aid for his affliction. But it seems more probable that deafness would have created a distaste for acoustics. If that was so, Edison's mastery of his revulsion, followed by great acoustical invention, becomes psychologically still more remarkable. The eminent British electrical engineer, J. A. Fleming, whose association with Edison will be mentioned presently, invented the first radio valve by the application of an electrical discovery made by Edison. As a component of electrical apparatus for sound amplification, the valve is perhaps the most important contribution to recent acoustical invention. Fleming, like Edison, suffered from deafness.

After the excitement of the invention of the phonograph, Edison looked for another suitable subject for inventive research. His friend Professor Barker suggested he should consider the problem of the subdivision of the electric light. By 1878 the electric arc-lamp had become commercially established, and was being rapidly developed. It was efficient, but could be made with commercial success only in large candle-powers. Its light was glaringly brilliant, and liable to flicker. These properties did not impair its use for lighting streets and railway yards, but prevented its use for the illumination

of offices and living-rooms. It was unable to compete with
the gas-light jets, which could be turned down to any desired
candle-power.

A practical small, steady, mild electric light would have
evident advantages. It would not blind or worry the eyes,
like arc-lights, nor pour the hot and often disagreeably
odorous products of burnt gas into room atmospheres pro-
viding air for the respiration of human occupants. Many
inventors were familiar with these considerations, and had
attempted, at least as early as 1841, to make small electric
lamps whose light was produced by a platinum wire raised
to white heat by an electric current. These attempts failed
owing to the relatively low melting point of platinum. The
platinum wire gave little light except near its melting point,
so any slight excess of current over the strength needed to
give light immediately fused the wire. It was not possible
in practice to evade such slight current fluctuations. Some
inventors tried to find less easily melted materials which also
conducted electricity. Carbon was an obvious material for
experiment, though its fragility and combustibility in air at
high temperatures were very serious defects. A carbon incandescent electric lamp was made in 1860 by J. W. Swan, a
pharmaceutical chemist of Newcastle-on-Tyne, England. It
was not of practical value, as the carbon rapidly burned up.
Swan was unable to exhaust enough air from the bulb to
prevent combustion of the carbon, owing to the lack of a
sufficiently good vacuum pump.

The cost of electric current was another serious limitation
at that time, as all current was obtained from expensive
voltaic batteries. Until cheaper sources of current were
created, the electric lamp could not compete with gas. For
these reasons, Swan dropped his work on carbon electric
lamps. But the situation changed during the next seventeen
years. The progress of science and technology was being
delayed in many directions through the lack of high-vacuum
pumps. The general need brought forth the required instrument, when Sprengel invented his mercury pump in 1865.
This invention was essential for the creation of modern
physics, as it enabled physicists to make improved vacuum
tubes which led to the discovery of the cathode rays and the
electron.

The development of the railroads in the 1860's stimulated
the demand for illuminated railway yards for night working.
Serious fires in theatres emphasized the unsuitability of gas

for theatre illumination. These and other influences had increased the demand for arc-lamps, which in turn increased the demand for improved dynamos giving cheaper current. The self-exciting dynamo was invented about 1867, and Gramme rediscovered in 1870 the ring armature, giving steady currents, which had been invented some years previously by Pacinotti.

Swan returned to experiments on carbon electric lamps in 1877, with the assistance of C. H. Stearn, who was familiar with the latest advances in vacuum technique. He constructed and exhibited in 1878 a vacuum lamp with a carbon rod as the light-emitter. In 1880 he patented the process of heating the carbon filament during the exhaustion of the bulb, in order to drive occluded gases out of the carbon. This was the patent which prevented the development of the incandescent lamp in England without Swan's collaboration.

Edison's researches on electric lamps, started in the fall of 1878, led to the completion of a practical lamp in 1879. He found that he could not evade Swan's patent in England, so he wisely made terms with him. The carbon electric lamp was known in England as the " Ediswan " lamp. Edison's compromise with Swan proves that the incandescent carbon lamp is not exclusively his invention. The invention of the carbon incandescent lamp is often ascribed exclusively to Edison. This is inaccurate, and creates a false view of the history of science and technology, and even of Edison's greatness.

Swan produced a workable, though not commercially practicable, lamp. If Edison had never lived, Swan's lamp would probably have been gradually improved, and introduced commercially within the next thirty years. Edison made his lamp commercially successful, and so of practical use to humanity, within three years. This sociological achievement was more distinguished than his large share in the invention of the lamp. By inaccurately ascribing the invention wholly to him, his fame has been made to rest more in a priority he did not wholly possess, than in his unique practical inspiration. His invention of a complete direct current system was more important than the invention of the lamp. Edison's successes and failures in the development of the electric light present a balanced story far more impressive than the myth which ascribes the development entirely to him. His mistakes are even more inspiring than his achievements, because they reveal his common humanity, and destroy the illusion of omnipotence, created by misguided admirers, which is so discouraging to aspiring followers.

Edison worked on the improvement of the platinum lamp before he invented the phonograph. He tried to devise automatic controls which prevented the wire from being fused. He also tried to make incandescent sources consisting of particles of refractory substances, such as boron and chromium, set between conducting points. These were raised to a white heat by sending current through them. He dropped these experiments during the work on the phonograph, and did not return to the electric lamp until after his conversation with Barker. He now attacked the problem thoroughly. In his usual manner, he made a comprehensive collection of data of the scientific, technical, and economic aspects of illumination. He bought the back numbers of gas journals, and collected statistics of gas installations. He estimated the quantity of capital sunk in the world gas industry in 1879 at $1,500,000,000, drew graphs of the prices of iron and copper, of seasonal gas consumption, and so on. The price of coal at that time was about seventy-five cents, or three shillings a ton. This was one of the factors which enabled electric current to be made from steam power at a competitive price. These figures revealed the technical and economic position of the gas industry, with which a successful electric lamp industry would have to compete. They assisted him to calculate the minimum efficiency necessary in an electric lamp system for successful competition with gas.

He saw that the electric lamp should use as little volume of current as possible. If it used much current, the conductors for supplying the lamp system would have to be thick, and this would involve an excessive capital expenditure on the expensive metal, copper. Thus high-voltage and low-amperage lamps were desirable. But the voltage should not be too high, because high voltages are dangerous. This was particularly important at the beginning of domestic electrification. An excessive number of accidents then would have prejudiced the public against electricity. Edison and his assistants made detailed calculations and experiments on many of these points, and also on the precise structure of the filament and lamp. They systematically investigated the relations between electrical resistance, shape, and heat-radiation of filaments, and studied the specific heats of materials.

The effect of increasing the ratio of the resistance to the

radiating surface of a wire, by coiling it closely so that the coils obstructed each other's radiation, was examined by calculation and experiment. This work is particularly interesting in relation to the recent introduction of the " coiled coil " lamp, and shows Edison's grasp of the same principles of design nearly sixty years ago.

The reduction of the diameter of the filament by one-half increased the resistance four times, and reduced the surface to one-half. Thus the ratio of resistance to surface was increased eight times. A filament one sixty-fourth of an inch in diameter became incandescent with eight times less current than a filament one thirty-secondth of an inch in diameter. As a simple implication of the arithmetical relations between the resistance, radiating surface, and temperature of filaments, it followed that a reduction of the diameter of the lamp filament by one-half reduced the volume of current, and hence the amount of copper conductors, and the capital investment on copper conductors in an electric lighting system, by a factor of eight.

The quantitative approach of Edison's work on the electric lamp was of outstanding merit. Swan and others made carbon lamps which worked, but their researches, compared with Edison's, were qualitative. Their lamps worked irrespective of cost, while the costs of his were measured at every point.

Edison now energetically attacked the problem of making thin carbon filaments. He was very familiar with the properties of carbon owing to his researches on the carbon telephone transmitter. He succeeded first with a filament made from cotton sewing-thread, which remained incandescent for forty hours in an exhausted bulb. He tried thousands of carbon-containing materials, from tar to cheese. He experimented with six thousand different sorts of vegetable fibres, collected from all parts of the world. He found that bamboo gave the most durable filaments.

Sawyer and Man invented a method of treating the carbon filaments by heating them in coal gas. The carbon released by the decomposition of the gas by the heat settled on the filament and strengthened it, especially in the thinnest and therefore hottest places. This treatment simplified the manufacture of filaments uniform in shape and electrical properties, and helped to create the possibility of applying mass-production methods. After 1883, the process of making filaments by squirting a solution of cellulose, or cotton-wool, through holes began to supersede the bamboo process. The cellulose threads, resembling artificial silk, were carbonized in a closed box in a furnace, and then finished by the Sawyer and Man process.

The cost of Edison's researches up to the construction of his cotton-thread filament lamp had been about $40,000.

His experiments with lamps led to a first-class discovery in 1883. It had been noticed that the inside of bulbs containing carbon filaments gradually became blackened by a deposit of carbon. The blackening was not uniform, as a less blackened line was often left on the glass, in the plane of the carbon filament loop. This indicated that atoms of carbon were being shot off the filament, and that some parts of the filament obstructed the flight of atoms from other parts, so that all of the atoms did not directly reach the glass surface. Edison placed a small metal plate, held on a wire sealed through the bulb wall, between the legs of the carbon filament. The filament was then made incandescent by switching the lamp on in the usual way. He found that if the positive leg of the filament was connected through a galvanometer to the plate, a small current was registered, whereas no current was registered when the negative leg was connected to the plate. This experiment showed that an incandescent lamp could act as a valve which permitted negative, but not positive, electricity to pass. The phenomenon is known as the Edison Effect. He patented it, but did not investigate it further himself.

J. A. Fleming, who at the time, in 1883, was a scientific adviser to the Edison companies in London, began a long series of researches on the effect. With the discovery of the electron in 1896, the nature of the effect became much clearer. It was due to streams of electrons shot off from the hot carbon filament. By 1904 Fleming had recognized the possibility that the hot-filament lamp might be used as a valve or rectifier for obtaining direct currents from oscillatory currents of the type started by radio waves in radio receivers, and had constructed his thermionic valve for detecting radio waves. The addition of the third electrode, or grid, to the Fleming valve, by Lee de Forest, completed the invention of the modern radio valve.

The history of the Edison Effect and the radio valve shows how the demand for electric light, stimulated by the search for new directions for the investment of the swiftly increasing surplus capital produced by the exploitation of America, incidentally revealed information which assisted the invention of new directions for the investment of surplus capital in the twentieth century. As H. S. Hatfield has explained, surplus capital is more attracted to the exploitation of new inventions, rather than the efficient exploitation of old inventions. It is easier to find capital for the exploitation of the spectacular than of other commodities equally profitable and often more useful. Hatfield considers that the progress of invention is not inevitable, and argues that the tendency to favour the exploitation of spectacular inventions may be a sign of the gradual cessation of invention in contemporary civilization. The relation of invention to the evolution of history is very imperfectly understood.

The incandescent electric lamp with bamboo filaments had commercial promise, so Edison now had to solve the complicated problem of designing and manufacturing a complete system of electric lighting. This involved the invention of practicable forms of glass bulbs, the manufacture of glass bulbs, vacuum-tight joints, interchangeable lamp sockets, cables and protected wiring, electric light brackets, and all the details of domestic wiring. He had to design a current meter for measuring the quantity of current used by each consumer, and fuses for protection against excess currents.

It was necessary to invent and design central electrical power stations. The incandescent electric lamp system required a combination of voltage and current characteristics of which there was little previous experience. Efficient new types of dynamo for supplying such currents had to be designed. It was necessary to work out the most economical networks of wires for distribution. Edison and J. Hopkinson devised almost simultaneously the three-wire system, which led to the saving of large quantities of copper, and therefore of capital. At this time the theory of electrical networks was primitive. Many electricians were not sure whether electric lamps could be worked in parallel. The eminent electrician of the British Post Office, W. H. Preece, believed for some time that the subdivision of an electric current among many lamps was theoretically impossible. It was believed that the balance of currents in the network would be upset when lights were switched in and out. Most of these errors were due to ignorance of electrical theory, but up to that time practical men had not needed much electrical theory, and electrical theorists had not come into contact with many practical problems except in telegraphy and arc lighting. The dynamos for delivering varying loads of current at constant voltages required original design. There was a fallacious belief that the internal resistance of a dynamo should be equal to that of its external circuit. This reduced its working efficiency to less than fifty per cent. Edison correctly decided to build big dynamos with very low internal resistance. He introduced mica laminated armatures and mica insulated commutators, and invented insulating tape.

On the other hand, he made elementary mistakes in design. He believed the magnetic field could be prevented from leaking from the magnets by encasing them in zinc. It is true that zinc is diamagnetic and is less permeable than air by lines of magnetic force, but the quantitative difference between the permeabilities of air and zinc is negligible, so no practical advantage is gained by zinc jackets for magnets. He erroneously believed, too, that multiple legs on the magnets, each separately wound with copper wires, were more efficient than single legs wound with one coil.

The state of dynamo and electric motor engineering about this time is illustrated by the accidental discovery, at a Viennese exhibition in 1873, that it was possible to drive a dynamo as an electric motor with current from a similar dynamo. Someone happened to connect a stationary Gramme dynamo to another Gramme dynamo driven by an engine, and found that the second dynamo began to drive the first as a motor. Before then, electricians had not reached the conception, which is the basis of the modern theory of electrical machinery, that the dynamo is a reversible engine.

The mistakes of principle in the design of the Edison dynamos were removed by J. Hopkinson, a British engineer with a thorough theoretical training. He worked out the theory of the magnetic circuit by calculation and experiment.

Edison was probably influenced in his adoption of direct current by his familiarity with it in telegraphy. He knew many of its properties from much experience, and it was easier to solve the numerous new problems of electrical engineering for direct current, than for the more complicated alternating current. He foresaw, for example, that there would be a demand for current to drive electric motors, charge storage batteries, and run arc-lamps. At that time alternating current could not be used for these purposes, so the demand for it would be less than for direct current. His choice securely launched the development of electrical current engineering. Alternating current has theoretical advantages over direct current, but is more difficult to handle. If Edison had tried to use alternating current in the first central electric supply systems, he might have experienced disasters which would have delayed the development of electrical current engineering for many years. He chose the safer way and succeeded with direct current. After success had been achieved with direct current, engineers could attack with greater confidence the problems of alternating current engineering, which are inherently more difficult.

The successful invention of central electrical power stations introduced electricity as a new commodity to the markét. Edison's companies sold electricity to the consumer in units measured by an electrolytic meter. They retailed electricity.

Many new electrical manufacturing industries were required to meet the demands for lamps, dynamos, cables, and fittings. Edison personally supervised the production side of the original factories supplying materials for his electric light systems. His business manager was Samuel Insull. When the factories had grown to employ several thousand men, Edison sold his interests to a syndicate organized by Henry Villard, which consolidated the factories as the Edison General Company.

Jay Gould and the financiers of the first period of exploitation of electricity, in the form of telegraphs, were succeeded by a different type in the second period of electrical exploitation, in which electricity became a commodity. The telegraphs of a country are analogous to the nerves of an organism, whereas electric power supply is analogous to the muscles. The telegraphs do not require massive and correspondingly expensive equipment, but their possession gives instant control over the life of the country. A relatively small amount of capital invested in telegraphs may give immense power. This is one of the explanations of the peculiar wildness of telegraph finance. Ownership of the capital of electricity supply companies also confers great influence on the life of a country, but as it involves far more capital than ownership of telegraphy, it is more stolid. The large quantities of fixed capital tend to produce more conservative conduct. This helps to explain why the growth of electricity supply has been accompanied by the evolution of a new type of financier in the electrical industries. Jay Gould and the leaders of telegraph finance have been succeeded by Owen Young and the leaders of electrical supply finance. A transitional type is seen in Samuel Insull. He became Edison's secretary in 1881 at the age of twenty-one, and learned the technique of finance when the Gould tradition was still the strongest. He had operated the first telephone exchange in London. He grew up with the new electricity supply industry and acquired the more cautious technique suitable to manipulators of a more stolid form of capital. As long as American business expanded without serious checks, he was very successful, but when the first profound crisis occurred, his position did not remain secure. The United States Government conducted an inquiry into his affairs and requested him to attend an examination. He did not voluntarily comply with this request, and ultimately was extradited from the Balkans to the United States, for public examination.

The leaders evolved in the later stage of the electricity supply industry, such as Young, have passed through the crisis with less difficulty, owing to their more stolid methods.

The growth of the electrical industry also provided more scope for engineers. Henry Ford was employed by one of the Edison power companies, and was introduced to Edison as a young man who had made an automobile. Ford states that the first understanding and encouragement he received in his development of the automobile came from Edison.

An indirect effect of Edison's development of the electrical engineering industry is seen in journalism. The demand for copper increased, and provided Hearst with a vast income from his copper mine. He was able to use his profits from copper in the development of his newspaper system, which, it is said, has not been profitable. The profits on copper pay for the losses on journalism.

To some degree, commodities choose the sort of inventors needed to develop them, and the sort of financiers needed to exploit them.

Edison developed new methods in manufacturing. He estimated the effective economic price of an article, and then aimed at manufacturing it in relation to that price. He had calculated that lamp sales should be successful at the price of 40 cents, so he offered to supply lamps to the electric light companies at 40 cents each, if they would contract to pay that price during the life of the lamp patents. This offer was accepted. The manufacture of his early lamps cost $1·25 each. In the first year he lost 70 cents on each of twenty thousand lamps. In the second year he lost 30 cents on each lamp, and in the third the loss had been brought down to 10 cents, by improved processes and machinery. In the fourth year the cost had been reduced to 37 cents, leaving a profit of 3 cents. The total profit in that year was sufficient to cover the total previous loss. Presently he reduced the manufacturing cost of the lamps, sold in millions at 40 cents, to 22 cents. He then sold the lamp factory to a Wall Street syndicate.

This method of selling at a fixed low price and then forcing the costs down by production in large quantities has been followed with particular success by Henry Ford in the manufacture of automobiles.

Edison states that the introduction of labour-replacing machinery contributed largely to the cheapening of production.

" When we started, one of the important processes had to be done by experts. This was the sealing-on of the part carrying the filament into the globe, which was rather a delicate operation in those days, and required several months of training before anyone could seal in a fair number of parts in a day. The men on this work considered themselves essential to the plant and became surly. They formed a union and made demands.

" I started in to see if it were not possible to do that operation by machinery. After feeling around for some days, I got a clue how to do it. I then put men on it I could trust, and made the preliminary machinery. That seemed to work pretty well. I then made another machine which did the work nicely. I then made a third machine. Then the union went out. It has been out ever since."

This is an example of the use of invention as a social weapon. Edison's description implies that the machine was invented in order to break strikes, and the reduction of the cost of lamp manufacture was incidental. The invention of the sealing-on machine was directly inspired by struggles between employer and employed, and reveals the limitations of the theory that invention is due to pure inventiveness, by analogy to the fallacious theory that discovery is due to pure curiosity.

Edison left Menlo Park about 1884, and built a large laboratory and house at West Orange, to which he moved in 1886, when he was thirty-nine years old. The change marked a profound alteration in many aspects of his life. His first wife had died in 1884, and he married a second time in 1886. His second wife was Mina Miller. She was twenty years old, and had been well educated. He began to live in a different social stratum. Large quantities of money passed through his hands. He spent most of it on experiments, but he also lived as comfortably as he wished. He became a public figure of world reputation. The inventive brilliance of his Menlo Park years passed as he approached forty years of age. The system of organized invention that he had created at Menlo Park was gradually transformed into more orthodox management of production factories. Edison's invention became less brilliant but the weight of organization and resources became much greater. The return in invention on effort and expenditure became much less. The new electricity corporations began to construct research laboratories as part of their equipment. This innovation was largely inspired by the example of Edison's inventions research laboratory, but it had an essential difference. Edison's laboratory was for general research on inventions. Its aims were not subordinated to the needs of any particular industry. The research in the new corporation laboratories was subordinated to the corporations' industrial interests. The results of research in corporation laboratories were disappointing for several decades, but have recently become more satisfactory, owing partly to the increasing importance of large-scale experiments. Powerful apparatus is now necessary in many branches of research. Million-volt transformers and high-tension rectifiers cannot be made without the wealth and manufacturing resources of large electrical factories. Brains and the skill of a few mechanics are no longer sufficient. The corporation laboratory has definite advantages under certain conditions. When these conditions arise, it naturally achieves results beyond the scope of the cleverest investigator dependent on his own resources.

Edison made many important inventions after 1886, but most of them experienced peculiar failures besides great successes. He made the first commercial motion-pictures in 1891. The history of the cinema is complicated and Edison's part has often been exaggerated, but it was noteworthy. He saw that Eastman's invention of the flexible film made the manufacture of motion-pictures practicable. The flexible film could be produced in long narrow ribbons bearing a sufficient number of pictures to create a sustained illusion of motion. Edison devised a camera for photographing moving subjects with continuous films. He made pairs of holes near the edges of the film to accommodate the teeth of wheels which moved the film forward. The width of the film and the size and distance of the holes were fixed by him, and remained the standard in the film industry for fifty years. He organized the first film studio. This consisted of a hut built on a pivot so that it could be turned to the sun, in order to facilitate photography. Short scenes of exchanges between boxers, and so on, were photographed. The pictures were not projected onto a screen by a projection apparatus. They were run through a machine inside a box with a peep-hole. The machine was started by putting a small coin in a slot. The spectator applied his eye to the peep-hole, and saw the subjects in motion. These boxes or kinetoscopes were erected in fair-grounds and similar places. Motion-pictures were commercially exploited for the first time with these machines. But they did not show motion pictures to audiences of unlimited size, and they were also very short. Edison treated his early motion-picture work as if it were trivial. He did not bother to patent his kinetoscope in England. He chose the lower grades of popular interests as subjects for his films. He aimed at inventing and manu-facturing motion-pictures which could be sold to the fair-ground public. Edison must receive some of the credit for creating the tradition of motion-pictures as a popular enter-tainment meeting the demands of the masses ; the quality which makes the cinema, in Lenin's view, the most important form of art. He must also bear some of the blame for the vulgarity of the cinema tradition, which has aimed so much at the worst instead of the best aspects of popular taste.

Edison's extended researches on the separation of iron ore by magnetic methods illustrate another combination of achievement and lack of foresight in his later period. He worked with enormous application for nine years on the separation of iron ore from rocks. He designed large crushers which ground the rock to powder. The iron ore was separated from the powder by systems of magnets. He developed the automatic conveyor system of handling the materials to a new degree. Henry Ford states that it was the most complete which had been designed up to that date. Edison's contribution to the development of manufacturing processes is again evident here. His iron ore separation works was successful until the discovery of the very rich ores of the Missabe Range. His vision of a process which would control the world steel industry disappeared, and his works had to be closed. He lost the whole of his savings, about

$2,000,000, in this failure. It is possible that magnetic separation will again be commercially valuable, when the very rich iron ore deposits have been exhausted. But Edison's insight into the geological aspects of the steel industry in his own time proved faulty.

When the iron ore works failed, he considered to what new object he might apply his knowledge of handling minerals. The rapid growth of the building industry suggested that the cement industry might provide suitable scope. He started cement manufacturing. His processes were not particularly original. His rational courage in turning immediately from iron ore to cement after a huge loss was the most remarkable feature of these activities. His interest in cement prompted him to devise methods of making houses by pouring cement into a suitable mould. He hoped that it would be possible to produce concrete houses in large numbers at a low price. He devised moulds made of unit sections which could be assembled in a variety of forms, so that the houses would be of many designs. His architectural conceptions were in consonance with some principles of modern functionalism.

During the first decade of the twentieth century he worked on the development of steel alkaline storage batteries. He gradually worked out an effective design, mainly by persistence. The alkaline battery had many ingenious features, but as a product of a mountain of labour and resource it was not outstanding. Forms of alkaline battery are much used in electric traction and in submarines. They store more energy per unit weight than lead batteries, and will safely discharge and charge far more rapidly, and will stand more rough usage, but give current at a much lower voltage.

Persistence had always been exceptionally prominent in his method of working, but as he became older, the subtler qualities of imagination and foresight declined first. This left the impression that his persistence became even more marked, and with age grew into obstinacy.

Like many great men who lived to a great age, he became a semi-mythical figure in his last years. He was continually consulted on all sorts of problems, and often gave advice of value below the magnitude of his reputation. This was natural, because the powers of his youth had declined, and the ideas and methods which had been so brilliantly successful fifty years before were no longer entirely suitable to modern circumstances.

Edison was granted over one thousand patents. About two hundred of these were concerned with telegraphy and telephones, and included duplex, quadruplex, and sextuplex systems, automatic and printing telegraphs.

Several hundred patents were granted to him for inventions connected with the incandescent electric lamp and the central electric power systems. These included dozens of patents concerning the design and manufacture of carbon filament lamps, of dynamos for supplying power stations, of systems of wiring, and the innumerable details of a complete electrical power supply system.

He was granted scores of patents for the design and manufacture of phonographs or gramophones, and all their parts, especially gramophone records.

Other large groups of patents were granted for the magnetic separation of iron ore and the manufacture of Portland cement.

He was granted dozens of patents in connection with his development of the alkaline accumulator battery.

Besides these whole classes of patents, he had others of a key nature. He had a patent for aerials, which was essential for the development of radio and was purchased by Marconi. He held key American patents in connection with the projection of motion-pictures.

He invented the dictaphone, the mimeograph, gummed paper for fastening parcels, and many other individual contrivances.

Most of these patents depended on an intimate acquaintance with the facts of science, especially in electricity and acoustics. They entitle their author to the claim of being a scientific inventor.

By virtue of the importance and variety of his work, including the absolutely original invention of the gramophone, which was the chief contribution towards the democratization of culture since the introduction of printing, he is the greatest inventor recorded in history.

BIBLIOGRAPHY

Edison: His Life and Inventions. F. L. Dyer, T. C. Martin, and
  W. H. Meadowcroft. 2 volumes. 1929.
Edison: His Life, His Work, His Genius. W. A. Simonds. 1935.
"Edison in His Laboratory." M. A. Rosanoff. *Harper's Maga-
  zine.* Volume 165. September, 1932.
Fifty Years of Electricity. J. A. Fleming. 1921.
"Edison": Obituary Notices. *Science.* January 15th, 1932.
My Friend Mr. Edison. Henry Ford, with Samuel Crowther. 1930.
The Irrational Knot. Bernard Shaw. 1905.
History of Telegraphy. J. J. Fahie. 1887.
A Popular History of American Inventions. W. B. Kaempffert. 2
  volumes. 1924.
Edison: The Man and His Work. G. S. Bryan. 1926.
Memoirs of a Scientific Life. J. A. Fleming. 1934.
A History of the Wireless Telegraph, 1838–1899. J. J. Fahie.
Imminent Dangers to Free Institutions of the United States. S. F. B.
  Morse. 1835.
Letters and Journals of S. F. B. Morse. E. L. Morse. 2 volumes.
  1914.
The Inventor and His World. H. Stafford Hatfield. 1933.
Personal Memoirs of U. S. Grant. 2 volumes. 1885.
A Chapter of Erie. C. F. Adams, Jr. 1869.

JOSIAH WILLARD GIBBS
1839–1903

J. WILLARD GIBBS

J. WILLARD GIBBS

I

THE PROBLEM OF GIBBS

AFTER the Annual Dinner of a British scientific society, held in London within the last decade, twenty or thirty of the members retired to a café in order to continue informal conversations on topics of common interest. A discussion presently arose on the relative importance of various famous scientific discoveries. Everyone became keenly interested in this many-sided question, and the arguments became more and more earnest and involved. After a time, one of the participants suggested that the results of the discussion might be clearer if they could be expressed in a mathematical form, such as a ballot. A ballot was accordingly organized, and each member was asked to write down, in order of importance, the names of the twenty scientists whom he conceived to be the greatest that have appeared since the Renaissance. The orders on the separate ballot papers were combined so as to give a collective order. In this way, the party's collective opinion on the names and order of the twenty greatest scientists since the Renaissance was ascertained.

Newton was the first name on the list. Darwin was second, and Faraday and Einstein were bracketed third. The next name was Willard Gibbs. His very high place was due not to a few votes which put him first, but to uniformly high placing by nearly all of the voters. Another interesting feature of the final list was the absence of the name of any botanist.

The majority of the voters were experimental biologists, with a few chemists, and one or two physicists and mathematicians. The high place given to Gibbs by the biologists was probably due to their belief that the next fundamental advance in their science will be due to discoveries of a Gibbsian type. The conception of living matter as a system in equilibrium is emphasized more and more by the progress of experimental biology. The biologists felt that the next fundamental discovery in their science will be due to a deeper insight into the mechanism of the equilibria of the physical and chemical reactions in living matter. As Gibbs had virtually created an exact science of systems of substances in chemical and physical equilibrium, and had determined a perspective which had already provided several profound advances in science, they felt that the best promise of solving their immediate fundamental problem lay in the attitude of Gibbs. They looked to it for the inspiration which would reveal how the substances and surfaces in living matter operate.

Chemists were naturally prepared to give him a high place for his comprehensive theory of chemical equilibrium, and physicists on account of his contributions to vector analysis and statistical mechanics.

The high reputation of Gibbs, among scientists, of which this incident is a small illustration, is in remarkable contrast to his lack of popular fame. New York University has a hall of fame, where memorials are erected to great Americans. The choice of the men who are to be remembered is made by a ballot. Gibbs' name has twice failed to receive enough votes for election. The explanation and significance of this paradox is the chief problem in the consideration of his life and work as a factor in modern civilization.

The degree of his popular obscurity is shown by various facts and stories. Irving Fisher, one of his pupils, writes that in his day the majority of the students at Yale " did not know of his existence, much less of his greatness." Fifty years after the publication of Gibbs' greatest work, Yale still had no memorial of him, apart from a bas-relief in the Old Sloane Physics Laboratory, presented by Walther Nernst, the German physical chemist. Adequate memorials of Gibbs have been established in the United States only very recently. Ostwald wrote that when the news arrived in the United States, that Willard Gibbs had been recognized in Europe as a great genius, many Americans congratulated his namesake Wolcott Gibbs, who had done good work, but was assuredly no genius. Wolcott Gibbs' name was far better known in America, and " without enquiries, as a matter of course, he was taken for the newly-discovered star, and had to accept great ovations from his delighted countrymen, about which probably no one was more surprised than himself. The misunderstanding was not resolved for some time, and Willard Gibbs successfully withstood any attempt to make him into a popular hero."

Gibbs' reputation was for long far higher in Europe than in the United States. Irving Fisher has described how, when he went to study in Berlin in 1893, he was abashed to find that the German mathematicians had never heard of any of the professors who had taught him mathematics at Yale, but that when he mentioned that he had attended Gibbs' lectures, they exclaimed : " Geebs, Geebs, jawohl, ausgezeichnet." (Gibbs, Gibbs, oh yes, excellent.)

In his recently published memoirs J. J. Thomson writes that he does not know of any case of a more intimate connection between a man and a university, than between Gibbs and Yale, and it was long before Yale recognized that he was a great man. Thomson says that he was not a success as a teacher of elementary students. " Indeed it is said that there was at one time a movement to replace him." His greatness was not fully appreciated by Yale until 1901, two years before he died, when the Royal Society of London bestowed on him its highest honour, the Copley medal. Thomson writes that he had personal experience of how little Gibbs' work was known in the United States. " When a new University was founded in 1887 the newly elected President came over to Europe to find Professors. He came to Cambridge and asked me if I could tell him of anyone who would make a good Professor of Molecular Physics. I said, ' You need not come to England for that ; the best man you could get is an American, Willard Gibbs.' ' Oh,' he said, ' you mean Wolcott Gibbs,' mentioning the prominent American chemist. ' No, I don't,' I said, ' I mean Willard Gibbs,' and I told him something about Gibbs' work. He sat thinking for a minute or two and then said, ' I'd like you to give me another name. Willard Gibbs can't be a man of much personal magnetism or I should have heard of him.' "

There are various stories which may be apocryphal and have no basis in particular fact. But such stories gain currency only because they are consonant with what is known about the personality and circumstances of the subject. They are useful, if only secondary, guides to the psychology of the subject and the public attitude towards him.

Gibbs never married, and lived the latter half of his life in his eldest sister's home. Her husband was Addison Van Name, the Librarian of the college. This was an exceptionally important position at Yale, because the college had evolved out of a library formed by a number of ministers in New Haven, so the librarian's office was older than those of the professors. It is said that one of Gibbs' sisters was in the habit of commandeering Gibbs to drive her around the shops in the morning in the family buggy, on the ground that her husband, who was a busy man, could not afford the time. Whether or not this story is true, it is not incongruous with

Gibbs' character, for he could always find time to help others even in small things.

E. B. Wilson writes that Gibbs took his full share in the common duties of the home. In this connection he mentions the apocryphal story that Gibbs " always insisted on mixing the salad, on the ground that he was a better authority than the others on the equilibrium of heterogeneous substances."

He recounts the story that Gibbs was so modest that he blushed when someone referred to his letter in *Nature*, in which he had proved that an experiment proposed by Kelvin for the determination of the velocity of longitudinal waves in the ether was impossible.

Henry Adams towards the end of his life sought to introduce scientific modes of thought into the interpretation of history. He wrote that he looked about him in vain for a teacher. He thought of Gibbs, " the greatest of Americans, judged by his rank in science," who " stood on the same plane with the three or four greatest minds of his century."

As Gibbs never came to Washington, Adams had no chance of meeting him. But he heard from a friend that Gibbs had said that he had got most help in the problems of the philosophy of science from Karl Pearson's *Grammar of Science*, so he read this work. He found it interesting, but not original, and " never found out what it could have taught a master like Willard Gibbs."

The problem of Gibbs is the discovery of the explanations of his simultaneous greatness and obscurity, in terms of the condition of science in his time, the nature of his own work, the influence of his personal psychology and social environment, and the social history of the United States.

II

THE SIGNIFICANCE OF HIS CAREER

GIBBS grew up in an atmosphere of extreme devotion to an institution with conservative social ideals. The devotion which Yale could inspire is illustrated by the example of Benjamin Silliman. Shortly after he had graduated in law, he was asked by President Dwight to become the first professor of chemistry. He received the request as a command, and after being appointed to the chair, began to study chemistry. Like a Japanese Samurai, he placed his career at the service of the social institution to which he was devoted, and went abroad to acquire training.

In his case the sacrifice proved to be pleasant, as he found that he had natural aptitude for science, and became an influential scientist.

The chief aim of Yale education was to train a governing class for politics, religion, and commerce. It was similar to that of Oxford, but more intense and narrow in its method. Group-feeling was inculcated deeply, especially through the system of the students' life.

A scientist cannot occupy an important place in the life of Oxford University unless he has ability in academic politics. The same phenomenon existed at Yale. Until recently, scientists at Oxford were encysted there, and, as scientists, had little influence. The fundamental aim of the university was not the advancement of science. A scientist educated in such a system accepted the view that a scientific discovery could not be as important as training for government, and assumed that work in isolation and without influence was natural.

In the most characteristic Oxford and Yale social theories, science is conceived as a product of curiosity and play. It is a means by which members of a leisure class may satisfy curiosity and find amusement.

The conventional theory of liberal education which the Yale faculty expressed so clearly in 1871, and which will be described presently, embodies this view. The same view is implied in E. B. Wilson's remark that " Gibbs was not an advertiser for personal renown nor a propagandist for science ; he was a scholar, scion of an old scholarly family, living before the days when research had been *re*-search."

The old Oxford and Yale attitude towards science was natural in a pre-scientific age, but it is not appropriate when science has become an essential part of the social system. Gibbs did not perceive any contradiction between his acceptance of the social ideals of Yale and his recognition of the social value of multiple algebra, but this conflict suggests the chief explanation of the general failure to appreciate the importance of his work. He had insight into the nature of mathematics and science as social products with social uses, as he showed in his address on Multiple Algebra, but the body of persons in academic life which shared his views was not large enough to influence opinion.

He was not isolated by his academic colleagues through ill-will. He was esteemed highly, but not understood. He was appointed professor before he had published a paper. His colleagues made special efforts to finance the publication of his great memoir *On the Equilibrium of Heterogeneous Substances*. He was elected a member of the National Academy of Sciences at the age of forty, when the usual age of election was fifty. The Academy awarded its Rumford medal to him in 1881, when he was forty-two.

His colleagues were proud of him. His work was neglected because they could not understand its significance.

The view that the significance of Gibbs' work was not evident at the date of its publication is mistaken. As Maxwell pointed out with clarity and brilliance, his work was of the highest significance for chemists. The majority of educated men failed to see this, not because it was obscure, but because they were prevented by their preconceptions of the rôle of science in human activities, and also, but in a lesser degree, by the difficulty of Gibbs' method.

He used the logic of scientific argument with greater power than any of his contemporaries. Though his mathematics was simple, his contemporaries could not understand him because they could not follow his extremely concise and rigorous logic. But if they had had a better understanding of the significance of science they would have quickly recognized the importance of his work, in spite of the difficulty of the logic.

The failure to recognize Gibbs' achievement may have been due to the absence of any new principle in it. He merely worked out the remotest consequences of an existing principle, the second law of thermodynamics. If the work had contained a new principle, its novelty would have been more obvious, even if the principle and the results derived from it had been less important than the results that he obtained in his memoirs.

This is confirmed by the history of Einstein's theory of relativity. Einstein, like Newton and Gibbs, is a great synthetic thinker, who has produced a theory which comprehends whole regions of phenomena. The ideas and mathematics of the theory of relativity are, perhaps, more difficult than those of Gibbs' chemical thermodynamics, and yet Einstein and his work have quickly received the fullest recognition.

The recent history of quantum mechanics provides a still more apposite illustration. Among living leaders of science, the one whose qualities of synthetic power, rigour, and abstract thought most resemble those of Gibbs is P. A. M. Dirac. He has not been isolated. He received a Nobel prize at the age of thirty-one. Men have become more sensitive to the significance of new theories since 1876, because subsequent history has made the social significance of science much more plain. A much larger number of persons are now sensitive to developments in science, and insist on trying to understand the most recondite theories. If Gibbs' work had appeared in 1926 its neglect would not have been permitted. Large groups of research students would have been set to study it, and simplified expositions would not have been left to the enthusiasm of individual leaders of investigation.

The isolation of Gibbs was probably not entirely disadvantageous. It may have assisted his originality. If he had been a member of a large research school he might have been exposed to more conventional influences, and not have been allowed to choose his own giant theme.

Nernst contends that deductive science of the Gibbsian type, in which numerous conclusions are drawn from a few fundamental assumptions, gives more mental satisfaction than empirical science. This belief undoubtedly contributes to the immense prestige of synthetic theorists such as Newton, Gibbs, and Einstein. But it is questionable whether it has a sound foundation. The belief that theoretical deductions give more mental satisfaction than experimental discovery may be based on class psychology, and may not be inherent in the psychology of individual activity. It may have been inspired by the ancient social belief that living without working is more distinguished than having to earn a living. This would predispose one to believe that discovery by deduction, without apparent manual work, is more satisfying than discovery by manual experiment. That part of Gibbs' prestige which rests on this belief may have a false basis.

Nernst said that Gibbs' calculations were of too generalized a character to be capable of direct application to particular problems. He considered that the successful application of general principles to particular cases constituted a definite contribution to science, even when the application involved no addition to theoretical ideas.

Generalized thinking is not of industrial value if it is not made available by suitable technical inventions. Gibbs' work cannot be dissociated from that of the chemists and engineers whose inventions made it fruitful. Its value cannot be considered greater than the practical work which enabled it to have value.

Another reason for the neglect of Gibbs' work was the lack of experimental chemists and engineers of the sort who could make use of it. This lack was due to backwardness of industrial technique. Competition had not yet forced chemical industry to study the efficiency of its processes, and evolve a large number of the sort of technicians who could increase it. This was the sort who could have made use of Gibbs' results.

From the point of view of industry, Gibbs' work was neglected because it was too crude. The general theory of processes was given, but without enough detail to afford help to a works manager in any particular process.

The theory of the equilibrium of heterogeneous substances was a gigantic fruit brought forth by the mental needs of industrialism, but it was abandoned by its gardener before it was ripe. Gibbs did not attempt to ripen the fruit and make it palatable to technologists. This also contributed to the neglect of his work.

His lack of interest in interpreting his work may be related to his conception of his social rôle. He did not feel called upon to give his students introductory courses which would have made his lectures more intelligible.

His attitude in this matter may be contrasted with Maxwell's. Through the whole of his career, Maxwell gave special attention to lectures to working men. Such lectures formed a considerable part of his duties at King's College, London, in the period when he invented the electro-magnetic theory of light and the statistical theory of gases. Is it possible that Maxwell's intelligibility was a reward for social conscience, and that Gibbs' unintelligibility was a penalty for the belief that he had no duty to ensure that his discoveries were understood and used ?

Did Gibbs believe that he might be given by society the opportunity for research, without the obligation of explaining to those who supported him, the meaning and value of what he had found ?

If he had been educated to consider that he could have no right to enjoy the opportunity of research without seeing that his results were exploited for the benefit of those who supported him, he might not have been content to see his work neglected.

The continual rediscovery of Gibbs' results since the publication of his papers is one of the most remarkable incidents in the history of science. The leaders of scientific research in the 1870's do not appear to have taken thorough notice of what others were doing. The organization of the exchange of knowledge was inefficient in the age of extreme individualist competition. The leaders of research still had much of the psychology of heroes. They were the kings of the intellectual world, without obligation to submit their work to the criticism of the intellectual democracy, or take full notice of what happened at other courts.

Through these circumstances the aesthetic qualities of Gibbs' work have come to be more important than the wonderful collection of results contained in it. Nearly all of these results were rediscovered and given social value by others. But besides this value, Gibbs' work still possesses direct use. His form of the adsorption equation is superior to that discovered later by Thomson, which was too inexplicit to be really useful. Development has been made through the use of the Gibbs form, and by careful attention to the conditions implied by Gibbs.

The tendency in the modern theory of solutions has been to go back more and more directly to the original formulation by Gibbs.

The notion of activities introduced by G. N. Lewis in 1907 is a fairly exact expression of Gibbs' chemical potentials.

The great advances in solution chemistry since 1920 have been due to the abandonment of the van't Hoff–Ostwald conceptions and a return to the original Gibbsian method of determining the potentials in solutions, without preconceived ideas. The most convenient expression of the potentials is Lewis' notion of activities.

Gibbs' work remains as a gigantic and beautiful exhibition

of the power of the human intellect. The structure was not adequately used and appreciated when it was built. It is like a monument of the past which has been dug up, and reveals unsuspected human abilities. Many of the uses to which the monument might have been put are now supplied by a group of later and lesser buildings, but contemplation of it will always deepen the student's sense of what is possible to humanity.

III

HIS DESCENT AND EDUCATION

JOSIAH WILLARD GIBBS was born in New Haven in 1839. He was a member of a family which had been established in America by Robert Gibbs, the son of Sir Henry Gibbs, the proprietor of an estate at Honington, in Warwickshire, England. Robert Gibbs' mother was also a member of the English landed aristocracy, as she was a daughter of Sir Thomas Temple. The Temple family had been prominent in English governing circles for several generations. For reasons not known, the property of Sir Henry Gibbs was sequestrated in 1640, and his son Robert emigrated to Boston about 1658. Robert was loyal to Charles II, but subscribed to the popular religion of Massachusetts. His fourth son, Henry, graduated at Harvard in 1686, and became a minister. He showed " traits of obstinacy which seem to pretty generally characterize his descendants." Like other Harvard men of the time, he had a deplorably fanatical hatred of witches. His seventh child, Henry, graduated at Harvard in 1726, was librarian of the college in 1730, and later became a business man. His second wife was Katherine, a daughter of Hon. Josiah Willard, Secretary of Massachusetts Colony. Josiah Willard was an excellent man who earned the name of " the good secretary." His father was Samuel Willard, secretary, and in fact president, of Harvard.

Henry and Katherine Gibbs had a son named Henry, who also graduated at Harvard and presently had a son whom he named Josiah Willard Gibbs. This was the physicist's father.

Josiah Willard Gibbs senior was born in 1790 and graduated at Yale in 1809. He married Ann Van Cleve. He had five daughters, and one son. His third child was Julia, born in 1836, and the fourth, his son, was born in 1839, when he was forty-nine years old.

The physicist was the last of a line of six college graduates on his father's side, and on his mother's side there were also graduates, including the first President of the College of New Jersey (Princeton). When Josiah Willard Gibbs senior was studying at Yale, theology still had a higher prestige than other subjects, so he followed the usual theological course, though the thought of devoting himself to mathematics, for which he had much aptitude, had passed through his mind. His contemporaries commented on his extreme modesty and retiring disposition. He was licensed to preach, but rarely entered the pulpit.

The standard of theological study at Harvard and Yale had been high in the early part of the eighteenth century but by the beginning of the nineteenth century it had declined. The new studies of mathematics, classics, natural science, and English literature were attracting much of the intellectual energy formerly devoted almost exclusively to theology.

Gibbs felt, but did not accept, the attraction of the newer studies. As the study of theology was backward, there was scope for reviving it. The new impulse came from Germany, where Gesenius had recently stimulated the study of Hebrew. Stuart published a Hebrew grammar in the United States in 1821, which was based on Gesenius' work. As American printers had little acquaintance with Hebrew, Stuart had to set some of the type with his own fingers. Gibbs helped him with the correction of the proofs, and became infected with the enthusiasm for German scholarship, which was strong enough to inspire his teacher to learn the technique of printing. Gibbs gained a thorough knowledge of the German language and literature through his studies of German theological scholarship.

He was appointed professor of sacred literature at Yale. His mental attitude of logical criticism was in contrast with the dominating current of doctrinal theology. He disliked forming and avowing opinions, as he felt that " men have no right to hold correct opinions with the will, in disregard of what may be alleged against them ; and he disliked arbitrary judgments in respect to matters on which he had gained light only through candid and laborious study."

The style of his writings was clear. His logic was careful and his judgment sound, but he was inclined to be excessively averse to speculation. He could not manage the emotional aspects of intellectual appeal.

He had the ability of pursuing researches without intellectual companionship. He was particularly interested in the rationalistic theology of Eichhorn, whose name was hardly known even to his familiar friends. On the study of words, his chief work, he could achieve eloquence, though in general he did not possess " that magnetic power which inspires dullness itself." He wrote that " the analysis of sentences in the concentrated light of Grammar and Logic . . . brings one into the sanctuary of human thought. All else is but standing in the outer court. He who is without may indeed offer incense, but he who penetrates within worships and adores. It is here that the man of science, trained to close thought and clear vision, surveys the various objects of study, with a more expanded view and a more discriminating mind. It is here that the interpreter, accustomed to the force and freshness of natural language, is prepared to explain God's revealed word with more power and accuracy. It is here that the orator learns to wield with a heavier arm the weapons of his warfare. It is here that everyone who loves to think, beholds the deep things of the human spirit, and learns to regard with holy reverence, the sacred symbols of human thought."

He became the leading American scholar of his day on comparative grammar, and it is noticeable that he speaks of the grammarian as a " man of science." If he had been less modest, and more tactful, that is, less uncomfortably critical, he might also have gained a distinguished reputation in Biblical interpretation and archaeology.

The elder Gibbs' aversion to positive opinion did not arise from lack of moral courage. He was an ardent advocate of justice for negroes. He considered that the political arrangements concerning negroes had been made in the exclusive interests of the whites " as a combination and conspiracy of the ruling race." He expected " the judgments of heaven to fall upon the country " because the rights of the dumb millions were " scarcely brought into the account."

His manners were gentle. He was often absent in thought and taciturn, but was rather fond of social intercourse with his particular friends.

The elder Gibbs seems to have been a mathematician by nature who, owing to circumstances, had become a grammarian. He was interested in words as symbols, as things for expressing other things. His initiative was too much inhibited by the nature of his temperament to allow him to escape from the more conventional studies into those for which he was probably better endowed. He had difficulty in impressing his ideas and desires on others.

His son was educated at the Hopkins Grammar School from 1849 to 1854, and prepared for Yale College which he entered at the age of fifteen, considerably younger than the usual age. Josiah Willard Gibbs Jr. was a very successful student. He was second in his class, and won several prizes in

Latin and mathematics, and a scholarship for research. He presently wrote a thesis " On the Form of the Teeth of Wheels in Spur Gearing," and received a doctorate in 1863. During this period, in 1861, his father died. After he had received the doctorate, he was appointed a tutor at Yale.

The effect on Gibbs of the undergraduate atmosphere at Yale when he was a student may be considered in relation to the account of student life given by " A Graduate of '69 " in the year that Gibbs was a tutor in natural philosophy, and student life in his class was probably not much different from what it had been in Gibbs' class. Gibbs entered Yale at the age of fifteen in 1854, and graduated in 1858.

The chief feature of undergraduate life was the system of secret societies. American first, second, third, and fourth year students are named freshmen, sophomores, juniors, and seniors. When Gibbs entered the college, an ordered system of societies was in existence. The freshmen applied for membership in a freshmen's society. In his second year, he moved into a sophomore society, in the third, into a juniors', and in the fourth, into a seniors' society. The number of societies in each year or class multiplied. This led to competition between the societies for membership. The society representatives, or " runners," jumped onto the platforms of moving cars, fought the brakemen, and defied the police in order to meet the incoming candidates, and persuade them to pledge themselves immediately.

The initiation of a pledged man into his society occurred about a week after the commencement of term. Members in masks led him to the hall where the society held its secret meetings. He would be pushed into a dark room, where he would find other freshmen about to be initiated. When his turn came, members made up as horrific figures would blindfold him and lead him upstairs to an inquisitorial hall. After being asked nonsensical questions he was thrown into black empty space. He began to fall until he found himself caught and being tossed in a blanket. He may have been precipitated into a bucket of water, put into a pillory, laid on a mock guillotine, and then thrust into a coffin. Presently it was reopened and he was " recalled to life," and found himself initiated. The initiation was supposed to test his nerves, but not to hurt him.

The chief freshmen's societies in Gibbs' class were Kappa Sigma Epsilon and Delta Kappa. A third society was formed by the class of '59, one year junior to Gibbs' class. This was named Gamma Nu. It was started as an open society in defiance of the character of the existing societies. It slowly gained ground, in spite of efforts to break it up, because some of the best men joined it, out of contempt for the silly aspect of the activities of the secret societies. Gibbs was educated just before the reform began, in a period when the social prestige of the secret societies was extreme.

The members of one society specialized in hard-working scholarship, another in careless literary excellence, and another in good fellowship and sociability. The societies were comprehensive in membership. The process of differentiation began after the freshmen had been in residence for some time. The most prominent freshmen were asked to pledge themselves for election to sophomore societies. As less than a half of the freshmen were eventually elected, competition for places became keen. Men helped the election of their friends by canvassing and political bargaining. These elections drew a little between " society men " and " neutrals " who were not members.

The process of social selection continued through the elections to the junior, or third year, societies. According to the " Graduate of '69," these societies at that time were the most influential in college politics. They determined the election of the Wooden Spoon Committee and the five editors of the Yale Literary Magazine. The Committee elected the Spoon Man. They were supposed to choose the wittiest, most popular, and gentlemanly man of the class. The highest elective honour to which a student could aspire was the award of the Spoon.

The chief senior society was the " Skull and Bones," which was restricted to fifteen members.

The majority of undergraduates lived in rooms in private houses in New Haven. The strength of the societies was partly due to this. They provided social intercourse, which in universities such as Oxford is offered by the colleges. Undergraduates formed eating clubs for taking meals.

There was considerable roughness in the period when Gibbs was a student. The sophomores sometimes broke into a freshman's rooms. They began to smoke into his face, and he was made to sing or dance, and if he refused, he was stirred up with sticks named " bangers." The best way of scattering a crowd of sophomores trying to break into a room was to fire a pistol-shot through the door, after due warning.

Unpopular freshmen were " brought down " by " hazing."

They were overpowered, and their hair was cut off, or their faces marked with indelible ink, or they were stripped and covered with paint, and subjected to practices " which cannot be named." " Hazing " occurred less than once in each class, or year.

The sophomore and freshman classes engaged in " rushes." These consisted of mass fights in the streets.

Serious fights between young men of the town and the students occurred occasionally. Persons were killed in fights in 1854, and in 1858, the respective years in which Gibbs entered the college and graduated. In the first of these two fights the students discharged several pistol-shots into the crowd. The man who was leading the crowd fell down and died in a few minutes. It was found afterwards that he had been stabbed with a large dirk-knife, and had not been shot. The crowd secured the two guns of the local artillery company, and loaded them, with the intention of discharging them at one of the colleges. The police succeeded in spiking the guns before they were discharged. The identity of the person who killed the man was never discovered. The relations between students and townsmen were tense for some time before and after this riot. Students could not walk in the streets without danger or disturbance. Gibbs was fifteen or sixteen when this happened. What effect could such violent events have on a quiet youth ? Did they increase his shyness of society ? In any case, they must have made subjects like the higher mathematics seem remote. They may have contributed towards the creation of Gibbs' personal and intellectual isolation.

The row of 1858 began between students and firemen, or members of the fire brigade. After the fighting had grown wild, there was a cry of " Shoot ! Shoot ! " and several pistol-shots were discharged at the firemen. Their leader was shot, and died on the next day. He had a wife and two children, for whom five hundred dollars, or about one hundred pounds, was collected as compensation. Again, the person who killed the man was never identified. The students stood together very closely.

The progress of students' studies was tested by recitations before tutors. In mathematics recitations, the students worked at blackboards in front of the class. Many of the students devised ingenious methods of " skinning " or cheating. The " Graduate of '69 " says that in his class chemistry was skinned entire, and that hardly a smattering of the science was learned by anyone.

The examinations in mathematics inspired the greatest craftiness. In 1855, during Gibbs' student period, it is said that a skinner noted there was a cellar under the floor of the examination hall. When he had learnt where he would sit in the hall, he bored a hole from the cellar through the floor by his place. He arranged for a friend to sit in the cellar under the hole during the examination, with a complete set of reference books. He copied the difficult questions onto small pieces of paper which were lowered by a strong black thread to his friend below. When the friend had solved them, he hauled up the solutions with the thread, and copied them in his own handwriting.

In 1867 two professional burglars from New York were engaged by sophomores to steal the mathematics paper, but were unsuccessful.

The " Graduate of '69 " says that less than half the compositions handed in at language recitations were genuine, though, on the whole, honest work was the rule.

Literary achievement, especially by men of low position in the class, was esteemed by the students more highly than any other form of intellectual work. There were few contestants for the mathematics prizes, and their recipients were apt to be the objects of more or less good-natured chaff and banter.

The most characteristic feature of Yale college life was class feeling and class unity, i.e. the tendency of all the students of one year to act as a social unit. The extension of optional studies in the 1860's, which allowed students some opportunity to pursue those subjects which interested them most, was strongly opposed by many who believed it would undermine the social unity of the class. The aim was to make what were conceived to be good men with uniform social ideas, rather than good scholars or specialists of any sort. The prestige of sociability and good fellowship was higher than that of scholarship. This was reflected in the salaries of the professors, which were generally below the cost of the usual standard of living. Professors were willing to live at a financial loss for the sake of social prestige.

The Yale system of the 1850's and 1860's was a powerful machine for giving young men certain social characteristics. It was particularly suitable for training men of an active, extravert disposition for executive positions in politics, law, the church, and commerce. If the United States had not been growing and changing rapidly, and the number of Yale graduates had been larger, their history would have been different. They would have been governed by a type of politician even more thoroughly trained in clique management, and more undemocratic, than that produced by Oxford. The United States was too large, and the number of Yale men too small, for their government to pass entirely under the control of that group-loyal type. Students who passed through the system could not evade its profound influence.

Gibbs absorbed the Yale spirit completely. He accepted a set of social ideas of high value to a politician, but unsuited to a scientific discoverer. It increased his tendency to intellectual isolation, and at the same time, made that tendency seem natural.

He graduated just before the outbreak of the Civil War. His father died during the second year of the War, and he was able to continue research for his doctor's degree amid the excitement of the war atmosphere. He had already learned how to work in the atmosphere of the aggressive student life. During the first two years of his tutorship, and the last two years of the War, he taught Latin to undergraduates. These circumstances confirm that he was isolated from the popular social interests of his day. Though a young man, he appeared not to have been deeply moved by the profound social problems which provoked the Civil War. If he had, he would probably have taken some part in the struggle, even if too delicate to fight.

In 1865–1866 he changed to tutoring in natural philosophy. He and his sisters left the United States at the end of 1866, on a three-years visit to Europe. This implies that their finances had not been destroyed by the Civil War. No doubt they had inherited some means from their father, and these had not been lost during the financial crises of the War.

Gibbs was twenty-seven years old when he sailed for Europe. He was mature enough, given the ability and training, to acquire the maximum value from his experiences. He spent the winter of 1866–1867 in Paris, and then went to Berlin for a year, where he studied under Magnus, and attended lectures by Weierstrass and others. He went to Heidelberg, whose staff included Kirchhoff and Helmholtz at the time, in 1868. He returned to New Haven in June, 1869. He does not appear to have visited England for study, and never established a close personal connection with British culture.

Gibbs' published works show that he was under predomin-

antly German cultural influences.   He regarded Clausius and
Grassmann as his masters, and wrote in an abstract style more
German than any other.   He adopted the German manner of
professorial lecturing.   He gave far more attention to the
logical exposition of general principles than to the acquisition
of skill in the solution of particular problems, characteristic of
English university teaching.

It is not improbable that Gibbs owed in a large degree to
his father his receptiveness to German inspiration.   The elder
Gibbs was a profound scholar of German literature, and no
doubt arranged that his son had had a thorough grounding in
the German language.   A thorough knowledge of a modern
language has always been, and still is, rare among post-
graduate students.   Its cultural influence is not only larger,
but higher in kind, than that of a general working knowledge
of the language.   Gibbs was probably one of the rare students
with a knowledge of German sufficiently deep to receive
directly, from men such as Kirchhoff, the strongest impression
of the nature and style of German scientific thought.

His most famous work was on the equilibrium of heterogeneous substances, a subject which Kirchhoff had touched in
1855.

When he returned to New Haven in 1869, he was thirty
years old.   He was unmarried, and settled in the family of his
sister Julia, who was three years his senior.   The house had
been built by his father, and Gibbs remained in it to the end
of his life in 1903.   The psychologist may see in these facts
evidence of a mother-fixation.   Gibbs lived in a house which
was the symbol of the persistence of his father's authority, and
he lived in a back room under the benevolent control of his
elder sister, who was a substitute for his mother.

A psychoanalyst has pointed out to the writer that these
details, if they are correct, seem to show that Gibbs had trans-
ferred a strong regard for his mother onto his elder sister.   He
went to Europe in a family group in which his elder sister
probably had more authority, so his attitude towards her was
continued and confirmed, and not broken, during his visit to
Europe.

When he returned to New Haven and settled in her house,
he produced his great memoir *On the Equilibrium of Heterogeneous Substances* as an act of devotion to her, a sort of
spiritual child.   It is possible that she was unable to understand the full greatness of the gift.   If this were so, then it
might be possible to explain peculiar features of Gibbs' be-

haviour with regard to his work. He was abnormally modest about his achievements. Ostwald had considerable difficulty in arranging for the translation of his memoir into German. Gibbs seemed scarcely to care whether or not it was translated. He allowed the American separates of it to go out of print, and did not have them reprinted, in spite of requests from distinguished scientists in various parts of the world. Wilson mentions that for the first fifteen years after the completion of the memoir, Gibbs appeared not to have lectured on chemical dynamics. One may imagine that an author might rest from the study of a subject for a year or two, after a period of the intensest effort, but one may expect that after that, he would return to it with increased interest, and talk about it with his friends and pupils. It is possible that his lack of effective interest in the future and development of the chief child of his brain may have been due to the disappointment of an unconscious psychological motive.

At the date of Gibbs' return Woolsey, the distinguished President of Yale, was near retirement. It was felt that a number of developments, which would better adapt the college to modern needs, might be initiated simultaneously with the election of a new president. Yale had been founded by clergy with conservative tendencies, who had separated from Harvard in order to resume what they considered to be the doctrinal purity of Calvinism. The charter of 1701 had stated that the college was for instruction in " the arts and sciences " suitable for the preparation of persons " for public employment, both in church and state," but the clergy retained control over the college, and " believed theology the basis, security and test of the arts and sciences." The conservative tendency at Yale has never been lost, and has prompted the observation that " Harvard on the whole is radical and progressive—Yale conservative."

The writer in the Eleventh Edition of the *Encyclopaedia Britannica* says further that the strength of Yale college feelings and traditions were due to poverty. Professors at Yale were not expected to live on their salaries, but their high social position was supposed to assist them to marry well-to-do wives.

In his discourse on *The Relations of Yale to Letters and Science* Daniel Coit Gilman observes that Yale and Harvard were shaped after Oxford and Cambridge rather than the Scottish, French, and German universities, and that their " academic usages derived from medieval convents." The business of the early Harvard and Yale was to train two sets of leaders, for the church and state. Letters and science were not in their vocabulary, and religion and law were their chief subjects of study.

This system was gradually modified. At Yale a " chair of mathematics, physics, and astronomy was instituted thirty years before the professorship of ancient languages." Franklin presented them with an electrical machine in 1749, and later with one of Fahrenheit's thermometers. Fahrenheit was the first to observe the super-cooling of water. He described the phenomenon in 1724. Its theoretical explanation was first given by Gibbs. Early in the nineteenth century Benjamin Silliman was appointed a professor and went to Scotland to continue his studies. He started the *American Journal of Science and Arts*, and became for a period the most influential man of science in the United States. The Yale school of mineralogy became especially famous under James D. Dana, and the observation of the return of Halley's comet by Yale astronomers several weeks before it was seen in Europe stimulated the study of astronomy in the United States. H. A. Newton, whose obituary notice was written by Gibbs, made important researches on the origin of meteoric showers, and Loomis on storms. The first chair of agricultural chemistry in the United States was founded at Yale in 1846.

Yale had had two students who became outstanding in invention : Eli Whitney and S. F. B. Morse.

But this record was not sufficient, and by 1870 still more service for modern life was necessary. The faculties prepared a statement of the *Needs of the University* which was published in 1871. The writers state that the difficulties of the College have been increased by the " increase in number of pupils, and need for more instructors, from growing demands for more perfect education," and " to the great and general advance in prices " (after the Civil War), " which has taken from the older endowments a large fraction of their original value." They prepared a long list of desirable new chairs and extensions to buildings, and mentioned that the endowment of each new professor would cost fifty thousand dollars " even with the present compensation of three thousand dollars—less by one or two thousand than the well-established churches of New Haven think necessary for their ministers." They wished to increase the scope of Yale into that of a university. They discussed the needs of the Library first, as that was the oldest institution of the college. (Gibbs' brother-in-law was the Librarian.)

Their conception of education is expounded in their statement that " Central and most conspicuous among the Institutions organized by the President and Fellows of Yale College,
is the ancient school for liberal education, the Academical
Department, which *is* Yale College in the restricted sense in
which that name is commonly used. Its one aim is liberal
culture as distinguished from preparation for specific employ-
ments and pursuits,—a thorough education by mental discipline—the education which fitly precedes the study of any
liberal profession, and which is the *commune vinculum* of all
such professions."

Gibbs agreed with this conception, and his acceptance of it
helps to explain his detached attitude towards research. He
regarded research as an activity which helped to provide " a
thorough education by mental discipline," and he supposed
that the subject of research was of secondary importance, and
was the means to an end which was more important, mental
discipline.

Though the writers express their opinion of the superiority
of this sort of education, they discuss at length the importance
and the needs of the Sheffield Scientific School, which is for
" the study of the laws and forces of material nature ; and for
its distinctive method, instruction by object lessons." The
object of the school is to promote the study of natural science
and its practical applications, and training is given in civil and
mechanical engineering, chemistry, metallurgy, agriculture, geo-
logy, and natural history, and courses which " also lead to the
professional pursuit of architecture, mechanics and mining."

They compiled a list of new chairs and tutorships required
to extend the college teaching to the full scope of a university.
In particular, they stated that :

" A division is further required in the department of Natural Philosophy and Astronomy. At present the recitations
in Natural Philosophy are wholly conducted by tutors. But
a field so vast as that of Physics, and one in which the onward
march of science is so astonishingly rapid, demands the labors
of a professor who shall be permanently and exclusively devoted to it."

The new chair of Mathematical Physics was founded in
1871, and Gibbs was appointed as its first occupant. It is
notable that Clerk Maxwell was appointed the first Cavendish
Professor of Experimental Physics at Cambridge, England, in
1871. Why were new chairs of physics being founded in
widely separated parts of the world at the same date ? The

explanation is sociological. The first professorship at Yale was founded in 1755 for Sacred Theology, and the second in 1770 for Mathematics, Natural Philosophy, and Astronomy. At Cambridge, England, the chairs in theology were the oldest, and chairs in mathematics and astronomy were founded in the seventeenth and eighteenth centuries.

Why were chairs of astronomy founded at Yale and Cambridge in the eighteenth century, while chairs of physics were not founded until a hundred years later, in 1871 ? The explanation is that mathematical astronomy was the most important science in the eighteenth century, as ocean navigation is based on it. The Atlantic civilization of the eighteenth century was primarily mercantile, and founded on the shipping trade. Astronomy was the science of greatest value to it, and therefore received the greatest prestige. All men of education believed it was important. This sense of the importance of astronomy came from the pressure of the interest of the ruling classes. The awareness of the interest in it caused its importance to be accepted without question. Many able men studied astronomy without formulating to themselves reasons why they should. Isaac Newton was one of them. Newton and his discoveries in mathematical astronomy were a product of the urge of the ruling mercantile classes to discover how they could increase their knowledge of the technique of transport, and discover new sources of wealth, and increase their freights and profits.

Elihu Yale himself was a leading figure in the mercantile age, which produced Newton as the master theorist of the mathematical astronomy on which their navigation and profits depended. He amassed great wealth as Governor of the East India Company's settlement at Madras in India.

By the middle of the nineteenth century, mathematical astronomy was no longer the chief physical science. It was supplanted by theoretical and experimental physics, concerned with heat and electricity. The mercantilists had been replaced by a new ruling class of industrial manufacturers, who made goods with machinery driven by steam-engines, and conducted business communications by the electric telegraph. They wished their sons to learn something about heat and electricity, about the sciences of the steam-engine and the electric telegraph.

Clerk Maxwell's chair was created in 1871 for the study of the new physics. Before that date there had been no official courses of instruction at Cambridge on heat and electricity.

The Cambridge course was now adapted to the cultural needs of the new governing class. The sociological meaning of the foundation of Gibbs' chair at Yale in 1871 is the same. It was a move towards the adaptation of education at Yale to the needs of the new governing class of industrial capitalists in the United States.

The motives for the changes in courses of education are not always clear at the time they are made. The directors of educational policy who make original changes have a sense of what developments are needed from the general atmosphere of their time, long before the reasons for the changes are clear.

Gibbs' specialty was thermodynamics, which is the finest cultural expression of the age of steam. This branch of science evolved directly out of the invention, use, and improvement of the steam-engine. The chief founder of the science was Sadi Carnot, whose famous cycle is the ghost of the disembodied steam-engine. The leaders of the Industrial Revolution wanted more efficient steam-engines, and higher profits. This demand created the general impression that these matters were important, so scientists began to search for the fundamental principles which govern the working of steam-engines. Carnot, Mayer, Joule, Clausius, Rankine, and Kelvin accomplished this task, and professors were needed to teach this practically valuable new knowledge in the universities.

Gibbs learned all that these masters had discovered. As a student of thermodynamics he was a direct cultural product of the Industrial Revolution. But he did not complete the chapters they had written. He wrote a new chapter of his own. By the middle of the nineteenth century, the efficiency of the steam-engine had been considerably increased through the elucidation of its principles.

Similar refinements had not yet been made in the processes of industrial manufacture. The efficiency of steam-engines, and sources of power, had been increased by applying the laws of heat to them. No parallel increase in the efficiency of industrial processes, in which mixtures of all sorts of substances are boiled and heated together, was obtained by applying the laws of heat to them. No one had investigated, beyond slight beginnings, the theory of the effects of heat on mixtures of substances. A vast amount of empirical knowledge of what happens when mixtures of particular substances are heated had been collected, by experiment and observation, chemical factories, general industry, and research laboratories, but no theory of the phenomena had been worked out.

The possibility of conducting the chemical processes of industry efficiently depends on the discovery of such a theory. An efficient chemical industry, in which huge quantities of raw materials are converted into an enormous variety of finished materials, cannot be devised without a knowledge of chemical thermodynamics. The manufacturer must know exactly how much energy is consumed at each stage of his processes, if his costs are to be reduced to the minimum. He must have a science of chemical energetics which will give him this information.

Willard Gibbs virtually created this science of chemical energetics.

IV

THE EFFICIENT MANAGEMENT OF MIXTURES

As Isaac Newton supplied the scientific needs of the merchant traders of his day, Willard Gibbs supplied the scientific needs of the rationalizing and efficiency-hunting industrialists who have controlled Western civilization since the middle of the nineteenth century. This does not imply that Newton and Gibbs consciously supplied the most important cultural needs of the governing classes of their days, though, as will appear in Section V, Gibbs conceived mathematics as a tool for saving labour, and thus serving human interests. He probably owed this insight to the influence of the American general outlook on life.

The motives which direct men's private lives are largely unconscious. Perhaps not one-twentieth part of a man's motives for pursuing any particular course are clear to himself. The aim of the science of psychology is to reveal another twentieth or more to him, so that he shall understand himself better, and act more wisely.

The problems and aims of the study of the history of science are similar. Perhaps only one-twentieth part of the reasons why a scientist of a particular type appeared at a particular time and solved particular problems are clear to himself and his contemporaries. The aim of the historian of science is to reveal another twentieth or more of the concealed reasons why certain scientists appear at certain times and do certain things. Such knowledge gives a better understanding of the rôle of science in civilization, and helps to suggest the best method of managing science for the benefit of humanity.

When James Watt began to manufacture steam-engines, he was troubled by the lack of any convenient method of measuring their horse-power. He could not give prospective customers a reliable estimate of the horse-power, and hence of the value, of the engine whose purchase they were considering. In order to obtain more precise information of the amount of work done by the steam inside the engine cylinder, he devised about 1790 an instrument that he named an " indicator," which was essentially a pressure gauge, and indicated the pressure of the steam inside the cylinder. In 1796 someone, almost certainly his assistant, Southern, thought of attaching a pencil to the gauge, which would trace a line on a sheet of paper moved by the engine. This figure, or "indicator diagram," gave an automatic graph of the changes in the pressure and volume of the steam in the cylinder, and its area was a measure of the amount of work done by the steam. The indicator diagram and its properties had not been fully investigated by scientists before they were first obtained from a steam-engine. In a large degree, indicator diagrams were invented and drawn by the *steam-engine*, and presented to scientists for their consideration afterwards. The scientists did not invent the theory of heat and indicator diagrams first, and then specify how steam-engines might be constructed according to their principles.

They derived the science of thermodynamics from the indicator diagrams and other data put before them by profit-seeking engineers.

The pressure-volume diagram was one of the foundations of the science of thermodynamics. Pressures and volumes of steam were naturally studied first because they are among the most accessible properties of a quantity of steam. The other directly accessible property is temperature. Scientists presently began to use diagrams in three dimensions, which were capable of representing simultaneously the pressure, volume, and temperature of a quantity of steam. As a curve simultaneously represents pressure and volume in an ordinary indicator diagram, a surface simultaneously represents pressure, volume, and temperature in a three-dimensional diagram. Such pressure-volume-temperature surfaces were proposed and used by James Thomson in 1871.

Willard Gibbs began his original contributions to science by investigating the general theory of all such thermodynamical diagrams. Gibbs' researches grew directly out of science of the most practical character. He explains in the opening words of his first published paper : " Although geometrical representations of propositions in the thermodynamics of fluids are in general use, and have done good service in disseminating clear notions in this science, yet they have by no means received the extension in respect to variety and generality of which they are capable. So far as regards a general graphical method, which can exhibit at once all the thermodynamic properties of a fluid concerned in reversible processes, and serve alike for the demonstration of general theorems and the numerical solution of particular problems, it is the general if not the universal practice to use diagrams in which the rectilinear co-ordinates represent volume and pressure." He proceeds " to call attention to certain diagrams of different construction, which afford graphical methods co-extensive in their applications with that in ordinary use, and preferable to it in many cases in respect of distinctness, or of convenience."

He explains that other properties of a fluid besides pressure, volume, and temperature, may be used in order to specify its thermodynamic condition. One may also use the energy and the entropy of the fluid. As the existence of these properties was not known when the heat properties of fluids were first studied, pressure, volume, and temperature were naturally chosen for specifying the thermodynamic condition of fluids. But they are just as real physical entities as pressure, volume, and temperature. The notion of energy is now commonly understood. Heat itself is one of its forms. Entropy, which started as a mathematical formula, is now perceived to have a physical meaning. It is known from experience that heat tends to flow from hot to cold bodies, and that the material universe tends towards a uniform temperature. As the age of the material universe increases, the various packets of heat in it become undone, and their contents are scattered and shuffled until they are spread out evenly. Entropy is the measure of the degree of this scattering process. Among the unpublished notes left by Gibbs is a heading for a proposed chapter on " Entropy as mixed-up-ness." Eddington defines entropy as " the practical measure of the random element which can increase in the universe but can never decrease." Clerk Maxwell defines the entropy of a body " as a measurable quantity, such that when there is no communication of heat this quantity remains constant, but when heat enters or leaves the body the quantity increases or diminishes."

While entropy is not an obvious property of bodies, it may be handled exceedingly conveniently by mathematics. Gibbs suggested that this quality should be exploited in thermo-dynamical diagrams by choosing entropy as one of the properties by which the condition of a body may be defined. One may construct entropy-temperature diagrams, entropy-volume diagrams, entropy - and - logarithms - of - temperature diagrams, etc. He systematically explored the features of a variety of these diagrams. He found that a number of problems which could not be conveniently solved with the assistance of the old pressure-volume diagram, could be solved easily with the assistance of one or other of the new diagrams.

It appears that Gibbs was not the first to discuss the entropy-temperature diagram. T. Belpaire sketched the idea in a paper published in the previous year, 1872. But Gibbs handled it far more profoundly. It was also independently discovered by Macfarlane Gray, about 1876. He was the chief engineer of the British Royal Navy, and he was interested in its value to engineers. He gave it the name by which it is now universally known, the " theta-phi diagram." Through it the second law of thermodynamics and the notion of entropy were placed at the service of average engineers, who could not understand the abstract mathematical presentation of these principles in the standard works on thermodynamics. As Gibbs said, this diagram is " nothing more nor less than a geometrical representation of the second law of thermo-dynamics." The lines in the old pressure-volume diagram representing temperature and adiabaticity are curves difficult to draw. New curves must be drawn for each particular problem, and the axes are the only permanent lines in the diagram. In the theta-phi diagram the difficult curves need be drawn once only, as they are the permanent lines. The special lines which have to be drawn in order to find the solution of any particular problem are all straight, so the solution may be read off by inspection.

In addition, problems concerning wet steam and super-heated steam, of importance in connection with the perform-ance of steam-engines, may be solved on one continuous diagram, because it applies to mixtures of fluids, besides uniform fluids. The diagram would give information about the loss of efficiency due to incomplete expansion of the steam, whereas the indicator diagram gave only the work done on the piston, and the efficiency of valves and steam passages. The energy of the steam could be determined by simple measure-ment, instead of having to calculate an area from a number of measurements of curves.

Gray writes that the theta-phi diagram was suggested to himself by Sadi Carnot's water-wheel argument, which implies the principle of the diagram. In 1879 he began to use the diagram as an aid in teaching. In 1880 he used it in a public lecture, and was informed afterwards that Willard Gibbs had discussed it previously. He looked up Gibbs' paper and writes that he found it a " very high-class production."

One of the diagrams now most used by engineers is Mol-lier's modification of the theta-phi diagram.

Gibbs showed that his entropy-volume diagram was par-ticularly convenient for representing the thermodynamic condition of a body which consisted of a mixture of parts in different states, such as a mixture of ice, water, and water-vapour.

In his second paper he investigated the properties of thermodynamic diagrams in three dimensions. He extended the entropy-volume plane diagram by adding a co-ordinate for energy, and derived geometrical surfaces whose points represented simultaneously the volume, entropy, and energy of a body.

Thermodynamic diagrams and surfaces, in which entropy enters as a co-ordinate, have had a large part in the development of the science of low temperatures. This includes such achievements as the liquefaction of helium, and all that that has implied ; and the vast technical developments of refrigeration, which depend on the efficient expansion and contraction of varieties of substances and mixtures, such as ammonia, sulphurdioxide, and other refrigerants. Even the quick service of ice-cream and chilled champagne, the importation into Europe of beef and apples from Australia, and the functioning of the refrigerator in the domestic kitchen, owe something to Gibbs. Through the use of entropy as a co-ordinate in the surfaces, he was able to give a complete representation of the relations between volume, entropy, energy, pressure, and temperature for all states of the body. As Maxwell wrote : " The body itself need not be homogeneous either in chemical nature or in physical state. All that is necessary is that the whole should be at the same pressure and the same temperature." The tendency of the parts of a body, which were co-existent in different (solid, liquid, or gaseous) states, to change from one state into another, could be deduced from the surfaces, or perhaps more accurately, it was possible to deduce from the surfaces the conditions in which different parts of a body, such as a quantity of water, may coexist in different solid, liquid, and gaseous states, i.e. the conditions in which the body may exist as a mixture of ice, water, and water-vapour. With their assistance it is possible to give the theoretical explanation of a number of well-known and peculiar phenomena. When a liquid not in contact with its vapour is heated above its boiling point, or cooled below its freezing point, or when a solution of a salt or gas becomes supersaturated, the introduction of a small quantity of water-vapour to the superheated water will produce explosive boiling, while the introduction of a small piece of ice to the supercooled water will produce explosive freezing. A particle of salt-crystal will produce explosive crystallization in the supersaturated solution of salt, and a bubble of gas will produce explosive effervescence in the supersaturated solution of gas.

This behaviour of bodies in mixed states could be easily deduced from the thermodynamic surfaces, which showed that the parts of a body in one state might turn into another state suddenly. This occurred, under certain circumstances, when the parts were in two states, and in equilibrium. The introduction of a particle of the substance in the third state upset the equilibrium and produced an explosive change to a new equilibrium. The surfaces indicated the criteria which determined whether the equilibrium of the system was stable or unstable, and whether there would be a tendency for parts in one state to pass into another state.

Gibbs' researches on thermodynamic surfaces enabled him to discover a more general method of analysis. He gave all the results which appear in his first two papers in a much more general form in the third paper, on the equilibrium of heterogeneous substances. In this, he gives a discussion on the conditions of equilibrium which govern the formation of *new* bodies. The theory includes the explanation of the phenomena of superheating, supercooling, etc., in which new bodies, such as solid crystals, suddenly appear in solutions of solids. He explained that a fluid is stable if the formation of every possible new body in it, while the entropy and volume remain constant, requires an increase of energy. It is unstable if a new body could be formed having a lower energy. But it is possible that although there may be bodies which when formed in quantity would reduce the energy, so that the liquid is really unstable with respect to them, yet the formation of very small quantities would increase the energy, because an appreciable surface energy would also have to be taken into account. In that case the liquid is stable with respect to infinitesimal changes, but unstable with respect to finite changes. It will thus remain unchanged, unless one introduces some of the new body, when the necessity of the substance first appearing in an infinitesimal amount is obviated, and the way is open for a finite change to occur, which may be explosive.

Gibbs considered that the second law of thermodynamics should be placed at the beginning of the theory of heat, according to its importance, and explained that the introduction of entropy as a co-ordinate in thermodynamic diagrams helped to do this. He wrote that " the method in which the co-ordinates represent volume and pressure has a certain advantage in the simple and elementary character of the notions upon which it is based, and its analogy with Watt's indicator has doubtless contributed to render it popular. On the other hand, a method involving the notion of *entropy*, the very existence of which depends upon the second law of thermodynamics, will doubtless seem to many far-fetched, and may repel beginners as obscure and difficult of comprehension. This inconvenience is perhaps more than counter-balanced by the advantages of a method which makes the second law of thermodynamics so prominent, and gives it so clear and elementary an expression."

The two papers on graphical and geometrical methods of representing the thermodynamic properties of substances were published in 1873, when Gibbs was thirty-four years old. The authorities of Yale had appointed him a professor in 1871, when he was thirty-two, and had as yet published nothing. This shows that they had confidence in his intellectual ability and correct judgment.

The papers were original and elegant, and their merit was at once recognized by Clerk Maxwell. It would be interesting to know how Maxwell learned of their existence, as they were published in the obscure proceedings of the Connecticut Academy. Gibbs was not inclined to procure attention for his work, and would probably not have liked to send copies of it to Maxwell without request. But he may have done, or a colleague may have done so for him.

Maxwell's instant perception of the quality of Gibbs was not the least of his achievements. In 1874 he was very busy with the Cavendish Laboratory, which had just been designed, built, and opened under his direction. In 1873 he had published his *Treatise on Electricity and Magnetism*. He succeeded, amidst all these activities, in detecting the merit of the work of an unknown young man in a distant country whose inhabitants at the time were making few contributions to theoretical physics.

The most extraordinary feature of Maxwell's prescience is that he drew the attention of English *chemists* to the importance of Gibbs' work. In a lecture to the Chemical Society of London, on the Dynamical Evidence of the Molecular Constitution of Bodies, delivered on February 18th, 1875, he said :

" The purely thermodynamical relations of the different states of matter do not belong to our subject, as they are independent of particular theories about molecules. I must not, however, omit to mention a most important American contribution to this part of thermodynamics by Prof. Willard Gibbs, of Yale College, U.S., who has given us a remarkably simple and thoroughly satisfactory method of representing the relations of the different states of matter by means of a model. By means of this model, problems which had long resisted the efforts of myself and others may be solved at once."

Maxwell also drew attention to Gibbs' researches, in his articles on " Diffusion " and " Diagrams," in the *Encyclopaedia Britannica*. In the last paragraph of the latter article he describes the Indicator Diagram, and then concludes by mentioning that Gibbs has very completely illustrated the use of diagrams in thermodynamics, " but though his methods throw much light on the general theory of diagrams as a method of study, they belong rather to thermodynamics than to the present subject."

In spite of this recommendation the English chemists did not succeed in following Gibbs' work. They failed to appreciate his conceptions of chemical thermodynamics, which have provided the theory for the rational development of physical chemistry and chemical engineering. They missed the opportunity of exploiting the implications of his discoveries, and leading the creation of practical physical chemistry. The initiative passed to German, French, and Dutch chemists, who began to appreciate Gibbs' papers about ten years later, but were still in time to forestall the English. The body of chemical and physical research in the United States was not sufficiently developed to be able to take the first advantage of Gibbs' contributions. Gibbs' work was a product of the European rather than the American branch of the scientific activity of Atlantic civilization.

Maxwell died prematurely in 1879. He spent much time in his last years studying Gibbs' thermodynamic surfaces. He gave an exposition of their properties in his textbook on the *Theory of Heat*, and some practical details of how they might be constructed. He made a model of a surface with his own hands, and very shortly before he died, sent a plaster cast of it to Gibbs at New Haven. Gibbs received great pleasure from this distinguished gift, and highly valued the possession of it. The compliment to a young man on his first two papers, from the man whom many regard as the greatest physicist of the nineteenth century, was marvellous.

Maxwell's sympathy for Gibbs' work suggests that they had some similar methods of thought. Gibbs showed in his first papers that he could use geometrical illustrations to help the imagination without being tied to the obvious geometrical characteristics of bodies. The pioneers had put geometrical representations of pressure and volume directly onto paper. They tried to interpret phenomena by direct mechanical analogy. This method was pursued by Kelvin and others throughout their careers. They tried to explain all physical phenomena by analogy with simple machines, such as engines and springs and jellies, even when the analogy was not apt. This helps to explain why Kelvin had such a sense of failure at the end of his life. He had tried to explain the world in terms of simple machines, and the world was not, in fact, like a simple machine, so the analogy had led him into inextricable difficulties.

Gibbs and Maxwell were more subtle. They used geometrical and mechanical models when these had an analogy to some *part* of their problems, but they did not try to force the whole of their theories into forms of analogy to simple machines. Maxwell discovered his electro-magnetic theory of light with assistance from a model, which is described in his first papers on the theory, but he dispensed with the model when he had got what he wanted out of it. There is no reference to the model in his *Treatise on Electricity and Magnetism.*

The attitude of Maxwell and Gibbs, of using mechanical and geometrical illustrations, without following them slavishly, is consonant with that of contemporary physicists. The behaviour of atoms is investigated with the assistance of geometrical and mechanical analogies to parts of their behaviour, in so far as it resembles that of particles or waves, but the attempt to invent a complete model of an atom, which would operate according to the principles of simple machines, has been abandoned. The belief that the behaviour of atoms should necessarily be strictly analogous with the simple machines of common human experience is now seen to be an egocentric delusion.

Gibbs and Maxwell were both sensitive to elegance in research. Gibbs' elegance was stately and architectonic, whereas Maxwell's was brilliant and individual. Gibbs excelled Maxwell in rigour, but was inferior to him in striking practical exposition. Maxwell's early death was unfortunate for the prospects of Gibbs' work. He could present discoveries far more persuasively to those who did not know how to appreciate them in their original form. As will be described presently, Maxwell was equally swift in recognizing the merit of Gibbs' next memoir. If he had lived, and had continued to act, as it were, as Gibbs' intellectual publicity agent, the greatness of Gibbs' discoveries might have been understood ten years sooner, and physical chemistry and chemical industry today might have been twenty years in advance of its present development.

Through his study of thermodynamic diagrams and surfaces, Gibbs discovered how to elucidate the physical and chemical behaviour of mixtures of substances by thermodynamics. His models helped him to discover new aspects of systems, such as their thermodynamic potentials and free energies, and to represent them by new mathematical functions. As thermodynamics is concerned only with the energy and entropy, the conclusions concerning any system, which may be drawn with its help, are of a general nature. They are independent of any particular assumptions concerning the constitution of the materials of the system, and of any physical or chemical changes which occur in the system. Thermodynamics is concerned, as it were, with the public life of systems, and ignores their private life. This is the source of its strength and limitations as a method of investigation. General rules of behaviour may be defined by it, to which systems, whose private life may be of a complex and highly interesting character, must conform. The private peculiarities of such systems are often the most prominent and the first which engage the investigator's attention, but they are often also of baffling complexity, and impregnable to direct attack. It is often of great assistance to the investigator, whose chief interest may be in the private lives of systems, to be able to circumscribe those lives within public boundaries of some sort, even of the widest character. But it also often happens that a knowledge of the public boundaries is far too general to provide much insight into the private details of the system, which may be of chief practical interest, and in such cases, little can be accomplished through thermodynamics alone.

The science of thermodynamics was evolved out of the study of engines driven by steam. The first step towards generalization consisted of elucidating the principles of engines which were driven by any " working substance," or ideally perfect gas. Carnot, Mayer, Joule, Helmholtz, Clausius, Kelvin, and Rankine were naturally first interested in elucidating the laws for uniform, or homogeneous, substances. As the substances were uniform, the problem of the equilibria between their different portions did not arise. For example, the steam expanding inside the cylinder of a steam-engine is supposed to be in the same condition all through. It is not in one state at one end of the cylinder, and in another state at the other end. The founders of thermodynamics were inspired by the problem of the behaviour of steam inside an engine cylinder. They were interested in the work they could get out of the steam, what work it would do in public. They were not interested in the private life of the steam, the internal relations between its different portions. They assumed the states were the same all through.

The problem before a chemist is quite different. He is interested primarily in the reactions inside a flask, not in the work which can be got out of steam inside a cylinder. His primary interest is in the relations, the equilibria, between the various substances in the flask. The chemist is interested in equilibria, while the physicist, inspired by the engineer, is interested in the production of work.

Owing to the source of their inspiration, physicists first applied the laws of thermodynamics to the problem of the behaviour of uniform or homogeneous substances. They were not at first particularly interested in applying them to mixed, or heterogeneous systems, in which equilibrium between the parts is of primary importance. Consequently they did not specially study, though they did not ignore, the application of the laws to the problems of equilibria. Horstmann was the first to investigate chemical equilibria with the assistance of the principle that when a system is in equilibrium its entropy must be at a maximum. Gibbs began the publication of his vastly wider application of the same principle two months after the appearance of Horstmann's paper. He noted that little had been done " to develop the principle as a foundation for the general theory of thermodynamic equilibrium."

He set out to develop those aspects of thermodynamics which are of interest to chemists, besides physicists and engineers. He put Clausius' famous statement of the two laws, " Die Energie der Welt ist constant. Die Entropie der Welt strebt einem Maximum zu " (The energy of the world is constant. The entropy of the world tends to a maximum), at the head of his memoir, and devised a mathematical apparatus by which they could be employed to elucidate the stability and equilibria of mixtures, or heterogeneous systems. He did this through the notion of the thermodynamical and chemical potentials of the components of a system, or mixture. Massieu had introduced the notion of thermodynamic potentials in 1869, but Gibbs rediscovered them, and exploited them with vastly greater power.

The chemical potentials of the components of a system are simple functions of the masses and energies of the various components. Through them it is possible to introduce the masses of the components as the variables in the fundamental equation describing the behaviour of the system. Heterogeneous equilibrium cannot be handled without using mass as a variable. The introduction and powerful use of mass as a variable constitutes Gibbs' greatest achievement.

He had succeeded in stating the problems of thermodynamic equilibria in convenient mathematical forms. He now started to deduce with extraordinary logical power numerous important conclusions from those forms. His arguments were mainly logical, and expressed in simple mathematics.

The conclusions had a wide application to the substances which occur in nature, for these consist of assortments of solids, liquids, and gases approaching, or already in, equilibrium. The laws of thermodynamic equilibrium must be obeyed by the constituents of the primeval rocks which had solidified out of molten solutions in past geological times, the soil and the atmosphere, the substances in living bodies, liquids and the materials they hold in solution, solid solutions, which are of fundamental importance in metallurgy, and all systems which have non-uniform features.

L. J. Henderson, J. Loeb, Van Slyke, and O. Warburg have applied Gibbs' principles to the analysis of the equilibria of salts in the blood and other living systems.

Irving Fisher applied Gibbs' theories and vector methods to the study of equilibria in economics. The principle of equilibrium in exchanges in chemical reactions is logically the same as in the exchanges of goods between persons, upon which the structure and stability of human society depends. In this instance, Gibbs' discoveries are seen to exert a direct effect on the conceptions of the mechanism of human society.

In the first part of his analysis, Gibbs considered the conditions of equilibrium in a system whose parts were different (heterogeneous), and in contact, but influenced by gravity, electricity, distortion of those masses which were solid, or by capillary forces. He explained that the choice of which substances are to be regarded as components of the system may be determined entirely by convenience. " For example, in considering the equilibrium in a vessel containing water and free hydrogen and oxygen, we should be obliged to recognize three components in the gaseous part. But in considering the equilibrium of dilute sulphuric acid with the vapor which it yields, we should have only two components to consider in the liquid mass, sulphuric acid . . . and . . . water."

The conditions relating to the possible formation of masses unlike any previously existing in the system are then explored. It will be seen that these conditions would apply to phenomena such as the appearance and growth of crystals in a solution hitherto clear, the formation of ice in a system of water and water-vapour, etc.

The importance of Gibbs' memoir *On the Equilibrium of Heterogeneous Substances* was immediately recognized by Clerk Maxwell. He even began to lecture on it before its publication was completed. He expounded Gibbs' theory of chemical potentials on a remarkable public occasion in 1876. The first international loan exhibition of scientific apparatus which had even been organized was opened in that year at South Kensington, London, by Queen Victoria and the Empress of Germany. Historic apparatus was loaned from many countries, and many of the leading scientists of Europe attended, including Helmholtz, C. W. Siemens, Beilstein, Wöhler, Ewald-Herring, Andrews, Pictet, and von Ettinghausen, and conferences on many subjects were held for a fortnight. When Queen Victoria visited the exhibits, Clerk Maxwell himself demonstrated Otto von Guericke's original air-pump, and Magdeburg spheres, to her. On one day 11,969 persons visited the exhibits, and *The Times* devoted about twenty columns, spread over a few weeks, to the affairs of the exhibition. The Americans had not exhibited, as all of their material was at their Independence centenary exhibition. *The Times* dismissed Maxwell's lecture with the bare statement that he had spoken " On the Equilibrium of Heterogeneous Bodies." One wonders whether Helmholtz, Pictet, Thomson, Andrews, and the rest paid as little attention to his discourse. American interests had a poor showing on this occasion. No doubt the memories of 1776, and the duty of celebrating independence by the exhibition in the United States, prevented good Anglo-American co-operation over the London exhibition. In this way, political feelings may have balked adequate attention to Maxwell's recommendation of Gibbs' discoveries. If there had been a large contingent of Americans at South

Kensington they might have taken special interest in the exposition of the work of one of their countrymen, and not have allowed it to be practically ignored.

Maxwell published an abstract of virtually the same lecture in the *Proceedings of the Cambridge Philosophical Society* in 1876. This was two years before the publication of Gibbs' memoir had been completed. This abstract is included in Maxwell's *Collected Papers*, but there is an even more interesting one in the *American Journal of Science* for 1877. In the Cambridge abstract Maxwell wrote that Gibbs' methods in his memoir (he had read only the first part) " seem to me to throw a new light on Thermodynamics," and he wished " to point out to the Society " their value.

In the *American Journal* he is reported as saying that Gibbs' methods " seem to me to be more likely than any others to enable us, without any lengthy calculations, to comprehend the relations between the different physical and chemical states of bodies, and it is to these that I now wish to direct your attention."

He explains that Gibbs " takes as his principal function the energy of the fluid, as depending on its volume and entropy together with the masses . . . of its . . . components."

" By differentiating the energy with respect to the volume, we obtain the pressure of the fluid with the sign reversed ; by differentiating with respect to the entropy, we obtain the temperature on the thermodynamic scale ; and by differentiating with respect to the mass of any one of the component substances, we obtain what Professor Gibbs calls the potential of that substance in the mass considered.

" As this conception of the potential of a substance in a given homogeneous mass is a new one, and likely to become very important in the theory of chemistry," he proceeds to expound Gibbs' definition of it. He explains that " the pressure is the intensity of the tendency of the body to expand, the temperature is the intensity of its tendency to part with heat ; and the potential of any component substance is the intensity with which it tends to expel that substance from its mass."

The problem to be considered is : " Given a homogeneous mass in a certain phase, will it remain in that phase, or will the whole or part of it pass into some other phase ? "

Maxwell quotes Gibbs' criterion of equilibrium, that for all possible variations of the state of the system, which do not alter its entropy, the variation of its energy shall either vanish or be positive, and then says that through this, " Professor

Gibbs has made a most important contribution to science by giving us a mathematical expression for the stability of any given phase A of matter with respect to any other phase B."

In both abstracts there is an explanation of Guthrie's experiments, in which a solution of sodium chloride was solidified in three different ways by contact with three different substances, according to Gibbs' theory. In the Cambridge abstract the theory " was illustrated by Mr. Main's experiments on coexistent phases of mixtures of chloroform, alcohol and water."

Gibbs discussed the effect of a diaphragm which divides the system into two parts, and " is capable of supporting an excess of pressure on either side, and is permeable to some of the components and impermeable to others." This leads to the statement of the conditions of osmotic equilibrium. He deduced that the potentials of components which can permeate the membrane is the same on both sides, and that the pressure is not necessarily the same on both sides. He did not give any formula for the pressure differences, but he gave an expression for the potential of a solute as a function of the concentration, from which van't Hoff's law could be easily deduced. He did not make this deduction until 1897. Under the influence of van't Hoff, osmotic forces were regarded as the forces exerted by molecules of substances dissolved in liquids. Gibbs did not conceive them in this way, though it was commonly held for a long period. Gibbs conceived the osmotic pressure as merely the pressure which must be applied to ensure that the potentials of the diffusable substances are the same on both sides of the diaphragm.

F. G. Donnan has described himself as one of those who rediscovered some of Gibbs' arguments. Donnan derived his theory of membrane equilibrium in 1911 by applying Gibbs' method to a case which had not been thought of before. This is the case of a salt in which the membrane is permeable to one ion but not to the other. This particular problem could not have occurred to Gibbs, because the existence of ions in solution had not been established at the time.

In order to clarify the conception of the constitution of mixtures, Gibbs introduces the term " phase." " In considering the different homogeneous bodies which can be formed out of any set of component substances, it will be convenient to have a term which shall refer solely to the composition and thermodynamic state of any body without regard to its quantity or form. We may call such bodies as differ in composition or state different *phases* of the matter considered, regarding all bodies which differ only in quantity and form as different examples of the same phase. Phases which can exist together, the dividing surfaces being plane, in an equilibrium which does not depend upon passive resistance to change, we shall call *coexistent*."

He deduces, by means of his notion of chemical potentials, a rule governing the possible variations in a system of phases. " A system of r coexistent phases, each of which has the same n independently variable components is capable of $n + 2 - r$ variations of phase."

Gibbs devoted four pages to the discovery and proof of this rule. He gave no concrete illustrations of it and proceeded to other problems.

Van der Waals was one of the first to study the phase rule. He explained it to a young Dutch chemist named Roozeboom, who was in difficulties with the equilibria of gaseous hydrates and double ammonium salts, and worked out a special case as an example for him, that he might find it of assistance in his researches. Roozeboom spent a large part of the rest of his life on applying it to mixtures of substances. Through it, he predicted the existence of new substances. In 1899 he used it to interpret the properties of steel as a system of carbon and iron. Iron may exist in several forms, which may be regarded as phases. Thus the phase rule indicates how many of these phases and the carbon will, under various conditions, appear together. Before Roozeboom's achievement, the theory of the composition of alloys was in a muddle and had no adequate basis. His work was fundamental to the creation of modern alloy metallurgy, which is necessary for the production of aeroplanes and innumerable machines which depend on the use of alloys with special properties. As Bancroft writes : " The variation of the engineering properties, such as tensile strength, torsional resistance, ductility, etc. with varying concentrations and varying heat treatment, is a subject which can only be worked out satisfactorily with the phase rule as guide."

The true constitution of Portland cement was worked out with the phase rule.

In ignorance of Gibbs' rule, van't Hoff had discovered some limited forms of it independently. One section of his later researches consisted of the application of the complete rule to the interpretation of the huge salt deposits at Stassfurt. These are the world's chief source of potash. The growth of chemistry and chemical industry in Germany has been conditioned by their existence. Without them, Germany would probably not have become a great power capable of challenging the world. The composition of the deposits was of high economic importance, for it enabled estimates to be made of the quantities of the various components available for industrial use. The deposits had been made by the evaporation of an inland sea in a past age, but when solutions of samples of salts were evaporated, they did not reproduce a mixture of the same composition as the original sample. Van't Hoff and his colleagues analysed the problem by treating it as an example of equilibria between sulphates and chlorides of sodium, potassium, and calcium. They proved that the presence of the strange salts was due to the slow rate at which the evaporation had occurred in the past. They deduced from the order and solubilities of the salts in the deposits, the stages in the drying-up of the sea millions of years ago, and were able to determine how long the evaporation of the sea water had taken, and the temperature and pressure at which it had occurred.

It is said that the lives of the English explorers, Captain Scott and his party, were lost in the Antarctic owing to the ignorance of the phase rule. When they started on their return from the South Pole, they found that the fuel oil can in one of their depots was empty. The solder of the can contained tin, which may exist in different phases. At low temperatures block tin may fall into powder, and cans soldered with it become unsealed. This appears to have happened to the cans upon which Scott depended for survival.

The equilibria of many systems have been investigated over wide ranges of temperature and pressure. Tammann discovered that water could exist in solid forms other than ordinary ice. Bridgman has investigated the equilibrium of the water system up to pressures of 20,000 atmospheres, and has shown that five different sorts of ice may exist.

Roozeboom discovered that some solutions have two boiling points. Under certain conditions the boiling point of a system may change suddenly from one temperature to the other, producing explosive boiling. A. L. Day and E. T. Allen have explained the volcanism of Mount Lassen in California as due to a change of this type in a system of silicates.

One of the most spectacular applications of the phase rule occurred in England during the last war. There was a sudden vast demand for ammonium nitrate, which is the chief intermediate product in the manufacture of explosives. As this salt is obtained from mixtures of other salts, efficient methods of manufacturing it cannot be devised rapidly without the application of the phase rule. If the English had not been able to engage F. A. Freeth, who had studied phase rule applications in the Dutch school, to supervise the rapid organization of the necessary processes, which he worked out graphically with the phase rule, they might have lost the war at an early stage, owing to shortage of explosives.

G. Tammann, who assumes the conventional view that the advance of technology is inspired by the prior advance of science, wrote that no abstract work has had such decisive influence on the development of basic industries as Gibbs' memoir on heterogeneous equilibria. He considered it improbable that Gibbs thought of the application of his laws to metallurgy, ore-dressing, the manufacture of refractory materials, or the equilibria between liquid slags and molten metals. This occurred through the quality which distinguishes a general theory, of growing beyond its creator, and being applied to realms outside his imagination. This is how, Tammann thought, the modern scientific technique of smelting has grown out of the abstract researches of a theorist with little experience of the world.

The phase rule will always be of great practical value in determining the general outline of many types of manufacturing processes. It indicates how many phases will be present when any reaction is finished and equilibrium has been reached at definite temperatures and pressure. It does not indicate the rate or nature of the reactions, nor the chemical constitution of the components taking part in them. Gibbs invented it incidentally as a minor clarifying aid in the development of his investigation of the general theory of the equilibrium of mixtures. For him it was an accessory fashioned in his attack on an immense intellectual problem. He dismissed it in four pages, but others created industries and saved countries with its help.

Gibbs invented the triangle diagram for representing three-phase equilibria graphically. It was reinvented by G. Stokes twenty years later, who had adapted Maxwell's colour triangle diagram for the purpose.

He analysed the conditions which characterize the critical phases of substances, and what may happen when the conditions are altered. He attacked the thermodynamic problem of catalysis. In a section on the properties of solutions of gases, he virtually formulated van't Hoff's law of the osmotic pressure of dilute solutions. Van't Hoff inferred the law from the experimental observations of Pfeffer and others, whereas Gibbs had foreseen it deductively. In 1897, while solving one of Kelvin's difficulties, he showed that van't Hoff's law could be simply derived from his former work.

Mixtures contain components of different sorts. The surfaces, or interfaces, between the components are characteristic of mixtures, and have an essential rôle in their properties. Gibbs therefore analysed the theory of interfaces, and incidentally founded the thermodynamical theory of surface tension and capillarity, and hence of colloid chemistry. He gave an exact theory of the structure of the black spot in very thin soap films.

He investigated the theory of the forces at the surfaces of liquids and substances, which tend to concentrate molecules on the surface, and produce the phenomenon of " adsorption." When substances are dissolved in liquids they may become concentrated by adsorption on the liquid surface, and alter the magnitude of the tension of the surface. Gibbs gave an equation from which the size of this alteration could be calculated. It is fundamental in the theory of adsorption. The study and application of adsorption is now an important branch of chemical science. J. J. Thomson rediscovered Gibbs' adsorption equation ten years later, by a much less accurate method.

The ordinary electric battery or cell is one of the most interesting examples of a mixture or heterogeneous system. Gibbs applied thermodynamics to the elucidation of its mechanism, and showed that a theory of the battery proposed by Helmholtz was erroneous. In the course of his analysis of the cell Gibbs derived an equation, which is the most important in the application of thermodynamics to chemistry, for calculating the free energy of a system. It was rediscovered by Helmholtz four years later, and is named the Gibbs-Helmholtz equation.

In 1887, nine years after he had published his correct theory of the cells, Gibbs was invited to comment on a symposium of the British Association on electrolysis, to which many of the leading physicists had made erroneous contributions. He repeated his correct theory, with additions, in two letters. He considered the relation between the electrical energy produced by the cell and the energy of the chemical reaction going on in it. Kelvin had suggested that these are equal. This was an incorrect application of the first law of thermodynamics, because it assumed that no heat was absorbed or evolved in the cell itself. Probably no alternative was reasonable so long as there was nothing to indicate how much heat was so produced. Gibbs identified the electrical energy with the change in the free energy, by showing that the cell when working in a state of balance is a perfect thermodynamical machine. Hence the heat produced in the cell is the difference between the energy of the reaction and the free energy of the reaction.

Other important laws which may be simply derived from Gibbs' theory are Konowalow's theorem of " indifferent points," Raoult's law, and Curie's theory of " crystal habit."

Gibbs outlined a complete theory of the thermodynamics of heterogeneous substances. These are mixtures, and therefore include the commonest natural objects. As Larmor wrote, " he made a clean sweep " of the science of chemical energetics. Boltzmann said that Gibbs' feat was the greatest synthetic achievement in science since Newton's construction of the theory of universal gravitation. Newton's achievement established the principles by which the mechanics of human life could be handled most efficiently. Gibbs established the principles by which the materials of life and industry, which are mixtures, could be managed most efficiently.

V

THE USE OF MATHEMATICS

GIBBS was the Vice-President in 1886 of the American Association for the Advancement of Science. He delivered an address on Multiple Algebra, in which he expounded his view of the nature of mathematics. He quoted with approval the statement that " the human mind has never invented a labor-saving machine equal to algebra," and said that " it is but natural and proper that an age like our own, characterized by the multiplication of labor-saving machinery, should be distinguished by an unexampled development of this most refined and most beautiful of machines."

He considered that the most characteristic development in his own day was in multiple algebra. There was much interest in it, whereas, fifty years earlier, the work of the founders of the subject, Möbius, Hamilton, Grassmann, and Saint-Venant, had failed to secure recognition in any way commensurate with its importance. Reversing Gibbs' argument, it is permissible to conclude that the failure to appreciate Möbius, Hamilton, Grassmann, and Saint-Venant was connected with the smaller development of labour-saving machinery in their day, and consequently less-developed conscious demand for labour-saving in all spheres of activity. The notion of economy in operations was not so strongly developed as in the age of Edison, and men had less conscious insight into the function of mathematics in civilization. The recognition that inventions apparently so different as multiple algebra and, say, the sewing-machine (Gibbs mentions the sewing-machine and reaper as examples of labour-saving contrivances later in his address) both sprang from attempts to satisfy the same social motive, the saving of labour, is fundamental for understanding the origin and rôle of mathematics in human society. Gibbs may have owed his insight into this matter partly to his American environment, where the social habit of invention was developed more noticeably than in Europe.

By classifying the invention of multiple algebra and of labour-saving machinery together, Gibbs implied that mathematical invention does not belong to a domain of human activity higher than that in which other labour-saving inventions are made. This was contrary to the traditional academic view, that the mental or spiritual quality of mathematics is higher than that of other human scientific activities. This view is still widespread, especially in popular writings on astronomy, in which the universe is represented as the materialization of abstract mathematical laws, if not the creation of a mathematician.

G. N. Lewis has quoted the story that Gibbs, during all the years of his membership in the Yale faculty, made one short speech only. After a prolonged discussion of the relative merits of studies in mathematics and in languages, as methods of education in culture, he arose and said merely, " Mathematics is a language." As this language was usually acquired late in life, it should not be used unnecessarily in place of the mother tongue, if an appearance of affectation was to be avoided.

Gibbs had a rationalistic and social conception of the nature of mathematics.

He quoted the history of the imaginary quantities of ordinary algebra, and pointed out that they were essentially a simple case of multiple algebra, in fact, double algebra. " This double algebra . . . was not sought for or invented (by mathematicians) . . . it forced itself, unbidden upon " their attention, " with its rules already formed." It arose out of the mathematics which had been devised for solving particular problems, such as those of trigonometry, which in turn had been invented in order to solve problems in practical affairs, such as navigation.

Double algebra " with difficulty obtained recognition in the first third of " the nineteenth century. Mathematicians at first regarded imaginary quantities, as the name they gave to them implies, as useless and awkward things thrust on them by a perverse external world. Instead of trying to see what aspects of the world these quantities reflected, they regarded them as a blemish in the creation. Mathematicians have often assumed that their laws are superior to experience, and have forgotten that they are labour-saving devices for describing the behaviour of the world. If they had examined the properties of imaginary quantities, or double algebra, without preconceived ideas of what mathematics and the external world ought to be like, they would have perceived, without so much unwillingness, that it could provide a more direct and economical method for solving many types of problems.

For instance, it may be desirable to analyse the behaviour-of a force acting in a plane. The force has size and direction. It may therefore be represented by a straight line, whose length represents the size, and whose direction represents the direction of the force. This directed line is one thing, and is named a *vector*, and may be represented by a single symbol. As this symbol contains in itself the simultaneous representation of two quantities, the system of calculating with it will be a double algebra, and the analysis of problems by the system is named vector analysis. The aim of multiple algebras or generalized vector analysis is to concentrate the representation of multiple properties into one symbol, and discover the laws governing the manipulation of this symbol. Gibbs said that the discussion of the forces and movements of particles, discussed in mechanics, physics, crystallography, astronomy, etc., seems to demand treatment by multiple algebra or vector analysis, because " position in space is essentially a multiple quantity and can only be represented by simple quantities in an arbitrary and cumbersome manner." Gibbs contended that the notions used in vector analysis are those which " he who reads between the lines will read on every paper of the greatest masters of analysis, or of those who have probed deepest the secrets of nature, the only difference being that the vector analyst, having regard for the weakness of the human intellect, does as the early painters, who wrote beneath their pictures ' This is a tree,' ' This is a horse.' "

He showed that Helmholtz's deduction of the motion of a fluid from its spin, which was regarded as a stroke of genius, could be solved by a beginner in vector analysis.

His vector methods have recently been applied to the design of electrical machinery, with important practical results. It is possible to reduce machinery design, with their aid, to the substitution of constants in general equations for any particular type of machine.

He aimed at the development of mathematical methods suited to the needs of physicists. He tried to look at physical phenomena without prejudice, and devise the algebras by which their properties could be most naturally and easily described. As Bumstead remarks, he had a " natural tendency toward elegance and conciseness of mathematical method." He was opposed to the indiscriminate application of old mathematical methods to new types of physical problems, merely because they happened to be at hand, and criticized the conservatism of mathematical astronomers, who failed to use vectorial methods in a subject which could be particularly amenable to them.

He explained that Lagrange and the greatest mathematical physicists unconsciously evolved new mathematical methods possessing some of the advantages of vector analysis. He wanted to see the search for improved methods in mathematical physics pursued consciously. The improvement of method is, in general, ultimately more fruitful than the solution of the most remarkable particular problems. According to Bumstead, Gibbs often remarked that he had more pleasure in the study of multiple algebra than in any other of his intellectual activities. This suggests that he was at heart a mathematician, which would help to explain his failure to expound effectively the practical significance of his deductive discoveries. But his account of his views of mathematics seems to show that he believed that the duty of mathematics was to assist the interpretation of physical phenomena. Pure mathematics was for him the most delightful of entertainments, but applied mathematics was of greater importance. He was a physical mathematician rather than a mathematical physicist.

Irving Fisher has written that Gibbs encountered the need of a new type of analysis through his attempts to represent physical relations, and the theory of electricity and magnetism, by geometrical methods. The old type of analysis with Cartesian co-ordinates required the writing and manipulation of three times as many equations as in vector analysis, and diverted attention away from the lines and surfaces which were of first interest to their projections on three arbitrary axes. Fisher considered Gibbs' most interesting lectures were on vector analysis. When he went to Berlin to continue his studies, he found that the German authorities did not care for vector analysis. Schwartz said " es ist zu willkürlich " (it is too arbitrary). They did not like a non-commutative algebra, such as vector analysis, in which $a \times b$ was not equal to $b \times a$, but to $- b \times a$.

Fisher reported this to Gibbs, after his return to the United States. Gibbs' view was that if the object is to interpret physical phenomena, and it is found that this can be done more conveniently by using such a non-commutative algebra, then the criticism was irrelevant.

Gibbs' attitude was similar to that of Heisenberg and Dirac in their researches on quantum mechanics. They considered the physical data which required theoretical explanation, and then devised appropriate mathematical methods for analysing their relations.

Gibbs told Hastings that if he had met with any success in mathematical physics, it was largely because he had found ways of avoiding mathematical difficulties. He did not consider mathematical difficulty a merit. One of his main motives was simplification of method, and he considered the perfection of vector analysis was a useful contribution to that end. He approached mathematics as a mathematical physicist rather than a mathematician, but he was not insensitive to purely mathematical interests. He had studied under Weierstrass and appreciated the attraction of rigour in proofs. He discovered the convergence property of the Fourier series known as the Gibbs phenomenon of convergence. But he considered, as Wilson says, that the " union between reflective analytical thought and the world of fact " is of more importance to the mathematical physicist than rigour in mathematical proof ; and believed that a superior training in pure mathematics was valuable because it assisted the study of the problems set by nature.

He regarded mathematics as a *language* for the discussion of nature. His views on the rôle of mathematics are similar to those expressed by Maxwell in 1871, in his inaugural lecture as first Cavendish Professor of Experimental Physics at Cambridge. He explains that knowledge which comes through the combined apprehension of its mathematical and its experimental aspects is " of a more solid, available and enduring kind than that possessed by the mere mathematician or the mere experimenter." New ideas can arise only by " wrenching the mind away from the symbols to the objects and from the objects back to the symbols. This is the price we have to pay." Maxwell writes that " there may be some mathematicians who pursue their studies entirely for their own sake. Most men, however, think that the chief use of mathematics is found in the interpretation of nature."

In spite of his realistic view of the use of mathematics, Gibbs 's not known to have made a single experiment.

The difficulty of his writing is due to his aim of generality. He always attempted to give general solutions of problems, which did not depend, for example, on particular assumptions about the constitution of matter. He wished to discover laws which physical systems of any constitution must obey. The ordinary investigator prefers to attack narrower problems, which have close analogy with particular phenomena with which he is acquainted, so that his imagination may receive support from the ideas with which he is already familiar. Gibbs was opposed to this method. He often said that " the whole is simpler than its parts." This is true, when the mind is capable of handling the symbolism, perhaps vector analysis, which conveniently exhibits phenomena as a whole, but it is not true for the mind which cannot handle such a symbolism, and has to use a less powerful, but less exacting, symbolism. Gibbs' aphorism expresses the essence of his intellectual attitude, and the essence of the method of thermodynamics.

VI

HIS PERSONALITY

GIBBS had a delicate constitution. He was the descendant of a long series of educated ancestors. Perhaps he was frail because his ancestors had chosen mental rather than physical qualities in mating, and he was the result of a persistent selection for intelligence. This selection ended in the production of a mind of the finest genius in a body apparently too weak to reproduce itself. E. B. Wilson comments that his grandfather died at the age of forty-seven, and his great-grandfather at fifty. H. A. Bumstead writes that he was permanently weakened by an attack of scarlet fever in childhood. He had a slight figure and voice, and in his later years frequently suffered from minor illnesses, but careful attention to his health, and regular living, protected him from any grave illness until shortly before his death at the age of sixty-four. His work was never seriously interrupted through illness. He used to spend summer vacations in the mountains, especially at Intervale, N.H., and in the evening after the day's work he often walked for an airing in the streets in the neighbourhood of the college.

He worked on his treatise on statistical mechanics in his last years. This may have sapped his strength, as Wilson suggests, for he could be seen working in his office on the second floor of the Old Sloane Laboratory in the morning, afternoon, and evening ; or he may have merely worked out his less than normal inborn supply of physical vigour, and died rather early. R. G. Van Name does not think that his death was quickened by overwork on the treatise, as he had recovered from that, when he was afflicted with an incurable intestinal obstruction. He told Wilson in 1902 that if he lived until he was as old as Methuselah, he would continue research for several hundred years. This shows that his zest and ideas were still vigorous. His head was impressive and he had an ingratiating smile. Former pupils report that he was unaffectedly modest, gentle, self-contained and dignified, and had no eccentricities.

His friends believed that he never realized that he had quite exceptional mental power. He justly estimated the value of his own researches, but he appeared to believe that almost any other person, who had had the desire, could have made the same discoveries.

He had complete confidence in the accuracy of everything that he published. Ostwald remarked that so far not one mistake in Gibbs' calculations, nor in his conclusions, nor, where mistakes are most difficult to avoid, in his general assumptions, had been found. G. N. Lewis has since noted, however, that Gibbs' view that some processes are of infinite slowness is not supported by experimental evidence. His mind seemed to work without special effort at the highest levels. Owing to its natural power he did not need to sacrifice any minor duties in order to secure more time for research. He instantly laid aside without question any profound work when called to perform minor tasks. He never evaded the most trivial college duties, or withheld any of his valuable time from students who sought his instruction. Wilson writes, however, that it was not customary for Yale professors at that date to give time to students outside the lecture hours. He asked Gibbs why he did not give preparatory courses which would have enabled students to follow his lectures better, and Gibbs replied that he had never felt called upon to do it, though he would if desired.

As he never married, he lived in the family of his sister, who occupied a house that had been built by his father. Apart from a single visit to Europe, he lived the whole of his life in New Haven, within a short distance of the school at which he had been educated, and the college where he had continued his education, and then taught. He had simple tastes and gave a full share of help in the common life of his sister's household.

He acted for many years as secretary and treasurer of the board of trustees of the Hopkins Grammar School, where he had been educated as a boy. He attended church regularly, but he took little part in social, religious, and political affairs. He rarely attended the Graduates' Club frequented by many of his colleagues, but he rarely missed any meeting of the mathematical and scientific societies and colloquia. He followed the proceedings keenly, but was always considerate in criticism. He did not despise papers of a light or entertaining character, and on one occasion read a paper to the Yale Mathematics Club on the mathematics of the " Paces of a Horse."

Wilson states that there was no trace of austerity in his

personality. An examination of his writings shows, however, that he had much intellectual firmness. In his controversy with Tait and others concerning the value and priority of Grassmann's methods over those of Hamilton's quaternions, his style and arguments were deadly. He was broad-minded and had a sensitive understanding. This is seen in the letter in which he replied to the request to write the obituary notice of Clausius.

New Haven June 10/89.
Professor J. P. Cooke

My dear Sir,
    The task which you propose is in many respects a pleasant one to me, although I have not much facility at that kind of writing, or indeed, at any kind. Of course, I should not expect to do justice to the subject, but I might do something.
    There are some drawbacks : of course it has not escaped your notice that it is a *very* delicate matter to write a notice of the work of Clausius. There are reputations to be respected, from Democritus downward, which may be hurt, if not of the distinguished men directly concerned, at least of their hot-headed partisans.
    Altogether I feel as if I had to take my life in my hands.
    Without making a positive engagement at this moment, as soon as I can get a little relief from some pressing duties, I will look the matter up and see what I can do, and will communicate with you further.
                                        Yours truly,
                                            J. W. G.

    This letter shows profound knowledge and judgment, generosity, humour, sensibility, and modesty. It was followed by one of the most remarkable obituary notices in scientific literature, which contains the classical statement of the origin of thermodynamics, and the extent of the contributions by the various founders. It is not surprising to learn that he was beloved by those who succeeded in acquiring his friendship.
    But he seemed to have some quality of deep isolation. Bumstead writes that he worked alone and apparently did not need the stimulation of discussion with equals or inferiors. He rarely told anyone what he was doing until his work was ready for publication, and he was chary of publishing anything unless he was convinced that it was a definitely original contribution to knowledge. His reluctance to publish an account of his system of vector analysis was due to this reason. He was not certain that it was not more than an adaptation of the work of others, rather than an original contribution.

As he did not discuss the progress of his researches with his advanced students, they had little opportunity of acquiring from him the mental attitude for research. They could not see his mind at work, and see how discoveries were made. He taught and explained his results admirably, but he did not reveal the processes by which he had discovered them.

This has a bearing on the great problem of Gibbs' career : his failure to make an immediate commanding impression on the contemporary scientific life of the United States. He had an inhibited temperament. Perhaps this prevented him from discussing his thoughts easily with others. But Wilson writes that he said in 1902 that during the thirty years of his professorship he had had only about half a dozen really equipped to profit by his courses. After he became professor in 1871, he lectured only to graduate students, and usually had an audience of about six or eight. Like a German professor, he did not set examples to his pupils on the matter of his lectures.

Wilson writes that Gibbs promised to discuss themes for research after he returned from further study in Europe, but unfortunately this never occurred, as Gibbs died shortly afterwards.

Wilson observes that the classical type of collegiate education was still almost universal during the greater part of Gibbs' professoriate, and this may have helped to prevent him from receiving many adequately trained research students.

He did not attract graduate research students from other universities to Yale, in spite of his later international reputation.

As Wilson asks, it would have been interesting to have seen what would have happened at Johns Hopkins University if he had accepted the invitation to a chair there, which was offered him when the University was founded in 1884. Johns Hopkins was a graduate university designed primarily for research, and Gibbs might have created a school of mathematical physics in such an environment.

His isolation may have been due more to his psychological temperament than to the nature of the intellectual environment at Yale. Like some other great isolated workers, he wrote very little, and thought problems out in his head. The great Oxford mathematician, H. J. S. Smith, who created no school, wrote the whole of his life's researches in a few notebooks. He used to think out problems in the theory of numbers while reclining on a sofa, and when, after hours of thought, he had found the solution, he wrote it straight down.

Joule wrote the descriptions of his researches almost straight out into four note-books. He also did not form a school.

After Gibbs' death, the papers he had left were found to be very meagre. They consisted mostly of headings for lectures. There were nine lines of intended supplements to chapters in his thermodynamical researches, with a brief sketch of some of the first and fourth chapters. It appeared that he composed his works in his head and then wrote them down. Wilson writes that he composed his *Statistical Mechanics* in a year virtually without notes, but from ideas he had carried in his head for some years.

As he carried the substance of his lectures in his head and did not write it out previously, he sometimes failed to prove his demonstrations on the blackboard at the first attempt. Wilson relates that he attended a lecture at which Gibbs became confused in an exposition of the Carnot cycle. Gibbs came to the next lecture with the chief points in the argument written on a small piece of paper.

Bumstead has related that he once saw a young research student enthusiastically recounting the result of a laborious experimental investigation. Gibbs unaffectedly and naturally closed his eyes for a few moments, and then said : " Yes, that would be true." He could calculate in his head from general principles the result that the student had obtained empirically by a lengthy research.

The intensity of the mental effort of this method of working may increase tendencies to introversion, and damage the sociability of the thinker in the world of ideas. It would be interesting to know whether there is any relation between a mathematician's ability for leading a school of research and his methods of discovery. Does the man who writes much, and uses much paper in attempts to find solutions, have closer intellectual contact with his students than the man who tends to think everything out before writing ?

Gibbs did not read exhaustively the literature of the subjects on which he worked. He often preferred to work out for himself results obtained by others, and said he found it easier than following another man's reasoning. It is significant in this connection that few succeeded in learning Gibbs' profound results from his own papers. Even Helmholtz and J. J. Thomson found it easier to rediscover his results than read his papers.

BIBLIOGRAPHY

The Collected Works of J. Willard Gibbs, Ph.D., LL.D. Formerly Professor of Mathematical Physics in Yale University. With a Biographical Sketch by H. A. Bumstead. 2 volumes. 1928.

Record of Celebration of the 200th Anniversary of Yale College. Edited by C. M. Lewis. 1902.

Four Years at Yale. By a Graduate of '69. 1871.

Memoirs of the Gibbs Family. Josiah Willard Gibbs. (A relative of the physicist.) 1879.

Modern Thermodynamics. E. A. Guggenheim. 1933.

Yale College: Needs of the University. Suggested by the Faculties to the Corporation & cont. 1871.

A Discourse Commemorative of the Life and Services of J. W. Gibbs, Senior. George P. Fisher. 1861.

" J. W. Gibbs and His Relation to Modern Science." F. H. Garrison. *Popular Scientific Monthly.* 1909.

" The Influence of J. Willard Gibbs on the Science of Physical Chemistry." F. G. Donnan. *Journal of the Franklin Institute.* 1925.

A Commentary on the Scientific Writings of J. Willard Gibbs. Edited by F. G. Donnan and A. Haas. 2 volumes. 1936.

Thermodynamics. G. N. Lewis and Merles Randall. 1923.

" J. Willard Gibbs and the Extension of the Principles of Thermodynamics." F. W. Stevens. *Science.* Volume 66. 1927.

" J. Willard Gibbs." R. C. Cantelo. *Canadian Chemistry and Metallurgy.* 1924.

Thermodynamics and Chemistry. P. Duhem. 1902.

Theory of Heat. J. Clerk Maxwell. Fourth Edition. 1875. (Adapted for the Use of Artisans and Students in Public and Science Schools.)

J. Clerk Maxwell. *Collected Papers.* 2 volumes. 1890.

" Regnault's Experiments on Steam." Macfarlane Gray. *Proceedings of the Institution of Mechanical Engineers.* 1889.

Metallography. C. H. Desh. 1922.

" Gibbs Memorial Lectures." *Proceedings of the American Mathematical Society.* 1923, & cont.

American Journal of Science. Volume 13. Third Series. 1877.

Obituary Notice in *Nature* of J. Willard Gibbs. 1903.

Obituary Notice of J. Willard Gibbs in *Proceedings of the Royal Society of London.* Volume 75. 1905.

" Willard Gibbs : An Appreciation." John Johnston. *Scientific Monthly.* Volume 26. 1928.

" Reminiscences of Gibbs by a Student and Colleague."　E. B.
　　Wilson.　*Scientific Monthly.*　Volume 32.　1931.
Chemish Weekblad.　Gibbs Memorial Number.　July, 1926.
Encyclopaedia Britannica.　11th Edition.
The Dictionary of American Biography.　1928 & cont.
Phase Rule Studies.　J. A. Wynfield Rhodes.　1933.
The Phase Rule.　A. C. D. Rivett.　1923.
The Phase Rule and Its Applications.　A. Findlay.　1935.

INDEX

Howard Coster

THE AUTHOR

J. G. CROWTHER, born in 1899, has travelled much, and visited scientific laboratories in many parts of the world. Has lectured at Harvard University on the History of Science, by invitation of the President. Was adviser on Technical Education to the Director of Higher Technical Education under the Supreme Economic Council of the U.S.S.R. in 1930.

Has made a popular science tour in the U.S.A. Is the author of *British Scientists of the Nineteenth Century* ; *An Outline of the Universe* ; *Soviet Science* (forthcoming in this series) ; *The Social Relations of Science* ; *Science in Soviet Russia* ; *Industry and Education in Soviet Russia* ; *The Progress of Science* ; *Science and Life* ; *About Petroleum* ; *The A B C of Chemistry* ; *Science for You* ; *Short Stories in Science* ; *Osiris and the Atom*.

His present job is writer and scientific correspondent of the *Manchester Guardian*.

PELICAN BOOKS

Advisory Editors: H. L. BEALES, Reader in Economic
History, University of London ; W. E. WILLIAMS,
Director, the Army Bureau of Current Affairs ;
Secretary, the British Institute of Adult Education

FAMOUS
AMERICAN MEN OF SCIENCE
BY J. G. CROWTHER

(II)

By Appointment

FRY'S

for

Good

Chocolate

★

D420.4542